FLYING ARMY

FLYING ARMY

The Modern Air Arm
of the U. S. Army

by W. E. BUTTERWORTH

Doubleday & Company, Inc., Garden City, New York, 1971

Library of Congress Catalog Card Number 77–137850
Copyright © 1971 by W. E. Butterworth
All Rights Reserved. Printed in the United States of America

I wish to thank all the people who helped me with this book. They know who they are, and they're the sort of people who would rather not be thanked in public.

Dedicating this book is difficult. At this writing, the closest thing I have to a little brother is flying a Huey in Vietnam. But I think that Major Cliff Walker, who wears three Distinguished Flying Crosses, and my other friends, will understand this:

To the memory of Captain Edwin Young III, who flew with distinction in Vietnam and crashed to his death in a training accident ten days before he was to return for a second tour, and,

to the memory of Richard I. Daniels, who crashed to his death in a Chinook five days before he was to return to active duty as a captain.

They, and the others who have flown their last flight, were young men of exceptional promise. Their sacrifice has made our country stronger, and they are not forgotten.

W. E. BUTTERWORTH

Fairhope, Alabama
November 1970

CONTENTS

FOREWORD

"Search and Destroy"

AT THE top of the operations order, beneath the red-stamped SECRET security classification, is the name of the operation: Operation Nancy Jane.

Beneath the title is the description:

Search and Destroy: Combat Assault.

In its simplest sense, Headquarters, Military Assistance Command, Vietnam (abbreviated MACV and pronounced Mach Vee) is ordering a brigade-sized unit, to go to a certain spot in Vietnam, to find either Viet Cong or regular North Viet Cong Army troops, and to destroy them.

The staff at MACV has determined that an enemy force exists at the target area.

The G-2 (*intelligence officer*) has acquired this information in any number of different, but complementing, ways. We employ spies, inside South Vietnam and in North Vietnam. The Air Force photographs and rephotographs every square inch of Vietnam, and the photographs are studied by photo reconnaissance interpreters. The Army duplicates this effort in their own area of responsibility, using both conventional photography and other means, including infrared devices on the Army's Grumman Mohawk, and other techniques and equipment still highly classified.

All of the information from all sources has been evaluated, tested, judged, refined, and has brought the intelligence officers to the conclusion that a force of so many men is at certain map coordinates.

At the staff meeting, the decision was made to attack the unit. The personnel officer reports that two battalions of a brigade of the division are up to strength and available. Supply officer reports that there are adequate supplies to mount such a mission. The Plans and Training officer draws up the plans for the operation.

One of the assistant staff officers, a crew-cutted first lieutenant eighteen months out of West Point, has just been notified that his wife has presented him with an eight-pound four-ounce daughter, who has been named, after her mother, Nancy Jane. That's as good a name as any, and Operation Nancy Jane, a Search and Destroy Mission involving two battalions of the 2nd Brigade, 1st Infantry Division comes to life.

A Helicopter-borne combat assault mission in progress. (*U. S. Army, Vietnam*)

A Grumman Mohawk reconnaissance airplane above the Mekong Delta.

(*Author's Collection*)

The Beechcraft U-8F. In Vietnam the entire aircraft is painted olive drab with black lettering. (*Beech Aircraft*)

CH-47 Chinook taking off from USS *Boxer*. (*U. S. Army*)

This is a small-scale operation, one of three scheduled for the same day. Actual command of the operation will be vested in the commanding general of the 1st Division. He, in turn, turns it over to one of his brigade commanders, a full bird colonel.

Telephone calls are made, and liaison visits between the units affected.

The Ground Tactical Commander, the full colonel commanding the brigade, flies to Headquarters, 12th Aviation Group, the aviations headquarters charged with providing III Corps with aviation support in a twin-engined U-21, differing from its civilian counterpart, the Beechcraft Kingaire, only in its paint job.

His counterpart officer of the 12th Aviation group, is on the ramp in front of the Base Operations when the U-21 rolls to a stop. They shake hands and go to lunch, the two grizzled bird colonels in jungle fatigues and boots and shoulder-holstered pistols carrying plastic laminate attaché cases that would be much more at home on Madison Avenue than here.

Overnight, the draft operations order has been prepared. This is not the first operation these officers have mounted. Nor the tenth. Closer to the fiftieth. They have developed a smooth functioning Standing Operating Procedure, or SOP. In a sense, all they and their subordinates have had to do is fill in the blanks on a form.

The attaché cases are opened. The operation is spelled out there in infinite detail. The target area is too far from the coast for naval gunfire, and too far from any of their own heavy artillery. That means that the pre-assault bombardment will have to be aerial. The Air Force, they decide, is good, but the Navy is better, and III Corps

An UH-1D "Suzy Q II" of the 118th Aviation Battalion. (*U. S. Army, Vietnam*)

has found them some available Naval Air from a carrier fifty miles at sea.

"Can the 12th Aviation Group give us enough Chinooks to simultaneously lift two batteries of 105s?" the 1st Infantry Division colonel asks.

"I can give you enough to lift them in, but not to simultaneously pull them out, if that becomes necessary," he is told. "Their secondary mission is fuel and ammo haul."

"How many to get them out?"

"One battery at a time. Eight Chinooks."

"I don't believe that we'll have to extract two batteries at once. That's fine with me."

Two companies of the 11th Combat Aviation Battalion, plus specific reinforcements are committed. The two companies break down into two platoons each of "Slick" Hueys (Bell UH-1D helicopters armed only with a machine gun in both sides in the doors). Each company also has attached a platoon of HueyCobras, the two-man helicopter gunships. There is also provision for a section of Medical Evacuation Slicks; for a Control and Command helicopter for each company, and for the companies together. The commanding officer's Huey is already set up as a flying command post, with radios installed in the rear of the machine giving him clear-channel communication with the Navy, with the Air Force, with the artillery, infantry, and medics on the ground, and with his own higher headquarters and the 12th Aviation Group. He can, of course, communicate with the leader, or any individual aircraft, involved in Operation Nancy Jane.

The exact time of the beginning of the operation is agreed upon. Everything from here on in will be scheduled in relation to M-Minute, H-Hour, D-Day. It's not nearly so complicated as it sounds.

The meeting lasts four hours. When it is over, Operation Nancy Jane awaits only its order of execution.

By noon the next day, it comes and M-Minute, H-Hour, D-Day is officially set.

Radio teletypes clatter at the 12th Aviation Group; at Headquarters 1st Infantry Division, and Headquarters, 1st Infantry Division Artillery; in the communications room of an aircraft carrier sailing in the South China Sea near Station Yankee. A messenger, traveling in a Huey, carries the word to the artillery battalion and the two infantry battalions involved. The Logistics Command informs the Quartermaster Petroleum Supply Point to start filling bladders for pickup and alerts the hospitals that an estimated blank number of casualties are to be expected.

Maps are distributed. An officer courier delivers the Signal Operating Instructions, the code names which will be used during Nancy Jane by all elements. These are Top Secret documents and passed between commissioned officers only.

In identical, air-conditioned buildings at various fields, the night-before briefings are held for the pilots of the helicopters. The Huey pilots are generally young and fresh looking. There's something about them rem-

The AH-1G HueyCobra. (*Bell Helicopter*)

Medical evacuation "slicks" in support of the South Vietnamese Army. (*Author's Collection*)

iniscent of the fighter pilots of War II glory. They're neater than their fathers had been, but just as dashing. They wear khaki baseball caps with their wings and warrant officer's bar, and they carry either .45 automatics, or .38 Special revolvers, or, less commonly, the S automatic M-16 rifle, although this is officially frowned on.

They sit in a briefing room while a commissioned officer, generally a young captain or a young major, but often a young lieutenant, explains the mission. They are given their aircraft chalk numbers, a number literally marked on their aircraft with a piece of chalk. This gives them their position in the flight, and their mission radio identification. The radio frequencies to be used are announced and written down.

They are told what they will do, when they will do it, how they will do it, and what they will do when they're finished.

There is little horseplay, for this is serious business.

The more experienced pilots fly the Chinooks, the Boeing-Vertol flying trucks used to haul cannon and fuel bladders around. The acknowledged best fly the huge Sikorsky Sky Cranes, which swoop in during an operation to pick up downed choppers like some mechanical eagle grabbing a tin rabbit.

This is not to say the normal Huey pilot is inexperienced. Once in Vietnam, 100 hours a month is routine; 150 common; more than that not unusual. They have been flying that many hours at maximum gross weight and more, day after day. They're good and they know they're good, but things still happen. There's always a lucky break for Victor Charley, or some clown who didn't get the word.

They earn their Air Medals, even if they

Huey pilots of the 25th Infantry Division in Vietnam being briefed.

(*PFC Charles Bart, U. S. Army*)

U. S. Army troops board CH-47 Chinooks for a combat assault mission in Vietnam.

(*Author's Collection*)

get so many of them (one for every twenty-five missions) that the number of them is sort of a family joke.

"Crank time is oh-four-forty-five," the very young major says. "That's all, gentlemen, thank you."

The chopper pilots file out of the briefing room. They run down the crew chiefs, and check on the bird. They go to their tents and damn the heat and the bugs. They go outside and watch the stars, and listen to the crump of artillery in the distance, and feel a little sorry for the infantry, out there eyeball to eyeball with Victor Charley.

A Sikorsky Sky Crane returns a shot-down Chinook to its base in Vietnam.

(*Sikorsky Aircraft*)

Inside a Vietnam Huey looking out as the troops begin to deploy. (*Author's Collection*)

Taking off to make the assault. (*U. S. Army, Vietnam*)

A Mohawk flashes overhead, possibly making still another infrared reconnaissance of the assault area. And then they go to bed, and wait for the Charge of Quarters to come in and wake them at quarter to four. The charge of quarters say that most of the chopper jockeys are already awake when they come by and turn on the lights.

At 0430, they're with their machines. By 0440, the pre-flight is done. At 0445, the co-pilot takes down the plastic laminated check list. The pilot turns on the intercom.

The co-pilot and the pilot mutter to each other about the position of the collective pitch and the throttle and the battery and the fuel warning light and the cyclic, and then, finally, the co-pilot reads, "Starter Ignition Switch," and the pilot says, "Pulled On and Holding."

The engine catches and the blades begin to revolve, and then start making the *fluckta-fluckta-fluckta* sound. The pilot pulls his mike switch back all the way to Transmit.

"Three cranked, Skipper," he reports.

"Roger, three. Stand by," the platoon leader answers. Operation Nancy Jane is under way.

ONE

Mr. Lowe's Balloon

History will show that the introduction of the helicopter as a weapons plat-
form and as a logistical transport will have as much effect on the conduct
of warfare as did the repeating rifle and the internal combustion engine.
COLONEL CHARLES A. MERRITT, *U. S. Army*

THE Army's use of aviation goes back beyond the airplane to the Civil War. In June 1861, Thaddeus Lowe, using a varnished silk balloon, rose on a tether over Washington, D.C., and came down again a few minutes later to report that Confederate forces were building earthworks and other fortifications.

Shortly afterward, James Allen made a similar ascension. Two other balloonists, John LaMountain and John Wise, also experimented with balloons, but only Allen and Lowe had an appreciable degree of success.

Lowe, who called himself "Professor" with just about as much right, and for much the same reasons as Samuel Colt of the revolver called himself "Professor Colt" and "Colonel Colt," was the most successful in convincing Army brass that he really had a military tool of worth, and not just a novelty.

Abraham Lincoln, who had had his own experience with senior Army officers when he was a captain in the Black Hawk War, was known to suspect the War Department of being resistant to military innovation. He had already had his battles with the Army over the introduction of Colt's revolving six-shot pistol, and Oliver Henry's repeating, cartridge rifle (which became the lever action Winchester).

In any event, Thaddeus S. C. Lowe's dealings with the military began at the top. On June 11, 1861, Lincoln talked with him at the White House. Lowe was assured by the Commander in Chief that the Army would give "serious consideration" to his proposals.

A week later, a varnished wicker basket

containing Lowe, an official of the local telegraph company, and a telegraph operator, rose five hundred feet above Alexandria, Virginia, beneath the balloon *Enterprise*.

The keys clicked. Via the Alexandria telegraph office and the War Department to the White House, and with certainly an eye toward history and public relations, the Commander in Chief was sent this message:

TO THE PRESIDENT OF THE UNITED STATES:
SIR

THIS POINT OF OBSERVATION COMMANDS AN AREA NEARLY 50 MILES IN DIAMETER. THE CITY, WITH ITS GIRDLE OF ENCAMPMENTS, PRESENTS A SUPERB SCENE. I HAVE PLEASURE IN SENDING YOU THIS FIRST DISPATCH EVER TELEGRAPHED FROM AN AERIAL STATION, AND IN ACKNOWLEDGING INDEBTEDNESS FOR YOUR ENCOURAGEMENT FOR THE OPPORTUNITY OF DEMONSTRATING THE AVAILABILITY OF THE SCIENCE OF AERONAUTICS IN THE MILITARY SERVICE OF THE COUNTRY.

T. S. C. LOWE

There may and probably were those in the military heirarchy who wished that Professor Lowe and his varnished silk gas bag would simply go away and let them go on with the serious business of waging war, but an observation point permitting a fifty-mile view simply could not be ignored.

Since the President already knew about it, and since he had proved his Indian fighter's temper already about the revolving pistol and the repeating rifle, there wasn't much really to do but cooperate.

The next day, June 19, 1861, Lowe's balloon rose from the White House lawn for the personal edification of the President and most of the Cabinet. Following the repeat performance, Lowe and his balloon were to be part of the Army, by presidential directive.

Professor Lowe, moreover, was much too wise in the ways of man and, especially, the military man to accept a commission in the Army. Officers, Lowe knew, could be assigned any sort of duty, including none, and officers' protests were not considered polite. He declined the commission, saying he would serve his country as a humble civilian.

Lowe and a hastily recruited and still unofficial "Balloon Corps" took the *Enterprise* across the aqueduct to Alexandria, Virginia, and made several ascensions in the hills near Fort Corcoran, across the Potomac from Georgetown. He made a few significant observations, and reported these to the ground by wrapping them around a Minié ball bullet and dropping them over the side.

After the Battle of Bull Run, that certain Union victory which turned out to be a Confederate victory, rumors ran through Washington of an impending massive Confederate assault. Lowe made a number of ascensions and reported that nothing he could see . . . and he could see practically everything . . . gave any suggestion that the Confederates were prepared for any further attacks. Not only did his observations do much to calm the near panic caused by the threat of the loss of Washington, but they also made unnecessary the expensive and difficult reinforcement of the capital already planned to rebuff the Confederate assault.

Even the Army became an ardent supporter of Professor Lowe now that he had proven the ability of the balloon to serve as an aerial spy. With hardly a murmur of disapproval the War Department, on August 2, 1861, authorized Lowe to acquire a 25,000-cubic-foot balloon. The new balloon, far larger than the *Enterprise,* was delivered on August 29, 1861. Christened, like a man of war, *The Union,* it was almost immediately sent aloft.

From *The Union,* over Fort Corcoran using a combination of telegraph messages and signal flags, on September 24, 1861, Lowe for the first time directed artillery fire. The efficiency of Lowe's method of artillery direction over the old method was so striking that the last resistance to this innovation vanished completely.

The next day, September 25, 1861, Secretary of War Edwin M. Stanton ordered the formation of the Balloon Corps of the Army of the Potomac, and named Thaddeus S. C. Lowe, Esq., Chief Aeronaut. The first order of business was to place an order for four more balloons.

By the new year, the Balloon Corps of the Army of the Potomac had seven balloons. When the Union forces pushed out of Washington, the balloons went with them.

"Even if they never saw anything," Confederate Brigadier General Edward P. Alexander said, after the war, "they were worth whatever they cost for the annoyance and delay they caused us in keeping our movements out of their sight."

In June 1862, the traditionists of the Army heirarchy were heard from again. A new branch of service was bad enough, but to have one commanded by a "Chief Aeronaut," rather than some reliable and predictable Army officer was simply beyond tolerance. It was decreed that henceforth the Balloon Corps would be part of the Signal Corps. Then the Signal Corps announced they had neither the funds, the experience, nor the personnel for such an operation. In June 1863 the Balloon Corps was disbanded.

The Confederacy, fully aware that balloons were a military innovation well worth copying, were having a hard time finding gunpowder and bullets for their guns. (The arsenal at Selma, Alabama, for example, formally requested the ladies of the town to save the contents of their chamber pots for use as a necessary ingredient in gun-

Brigadier General Adolphus W. Greely, Chief Signal Officer of U. S. Army, (1887–1906).
(*Defense Department*)

powder.) Manufacturing balloons looked virtually impossible, however desirable.

Despite all problems, however, the Confederacy managed to produce a few balloons and the gas for them. During 1862 balloonists Charles Cevor and Richard Wells rose above the Deep South and Captain John Randolph Bryan rose above Yorktown, Virginia. With these exceptions, however, the Confederacy had to fight without the benefit of the balloon.

The Balloon Corps, in its short life, proved beyond question the value of aerial observation for both intelligence purposes and the more elementary function of directing artillery fire. And it proved again that the military resists change with all the vigor of a reformed drunk turning down the offer of a bottle: Professor Lowe and most of the commanders of his Balloon

Colonel Theodore Roosevelt of the 1st U. S. Volunteer Cavalry in Cuba. (*U. S. Army*)

Corps spent far more time accusing one another of various character and professional deficiencies than they did sending balloons aloft or putting to use the intelligence the balloons provided.

When the Corps was disbanded officially, immediately after the war, the Army gave an almost visible sign of relief.

One junior officer, however, Adolphus W. Greely, could see beyond the friction the balloonists had raised. He saw it as a tool of warfare that should not, under any circumstances, be discarded. And he was wise enough to bide his time.

On March 3, 1887, twenty-two years after Lee said, "I would rather die a thousand deaths, but now I must ride to see General Grant," and surrendered the Army of Northern Virginia at Appomattox Courthouse, Greely was appointed Chief Signal Officer of the U. S. Army with the rank of brigadier general.

Five years later, after patiently laying his plans, and stilling the objections of the establishment, who thought they'd settled that aeronautic nonsense once and for all back in '63, Greely brought aviation back to the Army.

There was no argument whatever among the senior brass that communications had become an ever more important weapon. The prompt transmission of orders and the quick receipt of intelligence information was admittedly sound military thinking. Greely had no trouble in having "telegraph trains" authorized. The sole function of these trains was to provide field commanders with telegraph lines to their subordinate units and to their higher headquarters.

To support telegraphy, Greely argued, he needed a small balloon section to accompany each train. This might have been argumentative, but since it was General Greely, a soldier, and not some civilian thrust upon an unwilling Army as Lowe had been, it was accepted. Greely was part of the establishment; he could be trusted; if he said he wanted a balloon, let him have it.

In 1892, Lieutenant William A. Glassford of the Signal Corps was sent to Paris to negotiate with Lachambre et Cie. for a balloon. On delivery, it was named the *General Myer* after the first Chief of the Signal Corps.

In 1898 the United States went to war with Spain theoretically over Spanish oppression of Cuba, and specifically over the battleship *Maine,* which went down in Havana harbor after a still unexplained explosion. It was the only war the United States has ever entered with a will, as if it were a football game about to be played, rather than a bloody loss of life.

When President William McKinley showed less enthusiasm for going to war than Undersecretary of the Navy Theodore

Major General "Fighting Joe" Wheeler in
U. S. Army uniform. (*Signal Corps*)

Major Joseph E. Maxfield. (*Signal Corps*)

Roosevelt thought proper, Roosevelt said
publicly that McKinley had "less backbone
than a chocolate eclair." War was declared
to shouts of approval by the 55th Congress
of the United States. Roosevelt, declaring
that it would take him "at least thirty days
to learn enough to be a Colonel of Cavalry"
and announcing that he "proposed to be
fighting in Cuba within thirty days," mod-
estly accepted the lieutenant colonelcy of
the 1st United States Volunteer Cavalry
and reported to the Tampa Bay Hotel in
Tampa, Florida, and to the command of
Major General "Fighting Joe" Wheeler,
USA, late Major General Joseph Wheeler,
CSA.

Another officer reporting to the Tampa
Bay Headquarters was Major Joseph E.
Maxfield, Signal Corps, commanding officer
of the reborn Balloon Corps.

It wasn't much of a Balloon Corps. It
consisted of one modernized (it had a telephone, instead of a telegraph key) Civil
War model balloon, which had, according
to Major Maxfield, the appearance of a
"misshapen pumpkin." The *General Myer,*
for which Lieutenant Glassford had gone
to Paris, had been destroyed by high winds,
and when General Greely asked for replacement funds, he had been told that he had
been indulged once in his balloon nonsense,
but once was enough.

The misshapen pumpkin, moreover, had
been rushed to New York at the declaration
of war, to watch for the arrival of the
Spanish invasion fleet. By the time General
Greely managed to convince the New York
politicians that an invasion of Manhattan
Island by the Spanish was rather unlikely,
and then managed to convince the Cuban

Major General William Shafter.

(*Signal Corps*)

Expeditionary Force that they should have a balloon with them, it was almost too late.

The commanding officer of the Cuban Expeditionary Force was Major General William R. Shafter. He was stout to the point where the Remount Service failed him.

There wasn't a horse in the entire United States Army that would support him. He went to war in a buckboard.

He was supposed to take General Arthur MacArthur with him to Cuba, but the War Department sent MacArthur to the Philippines at the last minute, and the second most important general officer to go was Wheeler. Before he left for the West Coast, MacArthur arranged to smuggle a lieutenant aboard a troopship bound for Cuba against all military policy. Lieutenant John H. Parker had the odd idea that his particular weapon, the Gatling gun, might be of some value in the fighting there. He and the balloonists shared the same level of respect among the Cuba-bound forces.

MacArthur left for the West Coast, stopping only to say goodbye to his son, West Point Plebe Douglas, and the Cuban Expeditionary Force set sail for Cuba. The U. S. 1st Volunteer Cavalry, now known as the "Rough Riders," had been dismounted. When they began to suspect that they were going to be left out of the fun by the Regulars, trying to keep all the glory for themselves, Lieutenant Colonel Roosevelt solved their transportation problem by seizing the transport *Yucatan* at gunpoint and loading his men aboard.

The balloon *Santiago* being inflated in Cuba. (*Signal Corps*)

The balloon *Santiago* above the Aguadores River. (*Signal Corps*)

On the *Yucatan* went the balloon and the balloonists, the Gatling guns and their gunners.

The humidity of Cuba in the area of Santiago de Cuba promptly went to work on the varnished silk of the balloon. General Shafter, who had a quick mind in his heavy body, decided that the balloon, once it was there with him, was just what his Army needed. It was patched with surgical tape and sent aloft three times on June 30, 1898, providing Shafter with information about the Spanish fleet in Santiago Harbor, and on the roads leading to Kettle and San Juan Hills, the major Spanish fortifications between the Americans and Santiago itself.

The Americans became carried away with the efficiency of their airborne observation post. The next day, the balloon was ordered to the vanguard of the advancing American forces. And from it the observer dutifully reported the positions of the Spanish trenches and artillery.

But the Spaniards were aware that since there was only a narrow path through literally impenetrable jungle, it would follow that where the balloon was, so would be the American troops. They used the *Santiago* as an artillery aiming point. Spanish artillery fire was accurate and effective.

Aguadores River became Bloody Creek. A company of the 71st New York City Volunteer Infantry broke and ran.

The passengers in the *Santiago* were Lieutenant Colonel William Derby, the Expeditionary Force Engineer, and Major Maxfield, the commanding officer of the balloonists. Before the *Santiago* was shot down, Derby found an alternate road, and, by diverting the troops to it, and with the *Santiago* no longer serving as an aiming point, the efficacy of the Spanish artillery lowered, and then ceased.

The *Santiago* was through for that war, its bag ruptured beyond repair. But the officers now knew what the Spaniards had and where.

The next day came the Battles of Kettle and San Juan Hills. The Rough Riders, now under the command of Teddy Roosevelt, charged up Kettle Hill through the lines of the 10th Cavalry, a Regular Cavalry unit of proud Indian fighting reputation. With most of their white officers dead, including their commander, the colored cavalrymen of the 10th were too proud to let the Rough Riders gain all the glory. Without orders, they joined the assault on Kettle Hill. The only man on horseback was Roosevelt, and he was first man to the top.

Once Kettle Hill was theirs, they went down the far slope and headed for San Juan Hill. There, murderous Spanish fire pinned down other units of the Cuban Expeditionary Force until a new weapon, the Gatling gun which almost hadn't made it to Cuba at all, was brought into play.

It was admitted after the battle that without Lieutenant Parker's Gatling guns, the Battle of San Juan Hill would now be remembered as a Spanish victory. A captured Spanish officer reported that Parker's Gatlings had "cut us down like wheat before a reaper."

One other officer forgot himself that day in the heat of battle. Major General Wheeler, seeing that the tide was running for the Americans, turned and shouted with glee that "the damn Yankees are on the run."

During the Battle of San Juan Hill, the 71st New York earned itself a unique spot in American military tradition. Perhaps to redeem its honor (some of its riflemen had broke and run earlier) its company commander formed his troops in full view of the enemy, called them to attention, ordered them to port arms and marched them into battle, in step, counting cadence. Not one man broke, all the way to the crest of San Juan Hill. It is the only time American soldiers have ever done that.

Although only the *Santiago* actually got to Cuba, the Signal Corps ordered more balloons for its new air arm. After the war, they were stored in a warehouse at Fort Myer, Virginia. By the time General Greely was able to talk the establishment out of the necessary funds to use them, they had deteriorated beyond use.

It was 1907 before the Army got around to buying another new balloon. This was Number 9, the numbering system going back to the first balloon used by Thaddeus Lowe in 1861. On the heels of Number 9 came, on June 4, 1907, Signal Corps Balloon Number 10. General Greely built a hydrogen generating plant and a balloon house at Fort Omaha, Nebraska, the next year. Omaha would later figure in aviation as the headquarters of the Strategic Air Command.

But not all of the Signal Corps' aviation effort, which is really to say, not all of the military and naval aviation effort, was directed toward balloons. Some members of Congress at the turn of the century, admittedly influenced by Jules Verne, began to consider flying machines, vehicles which would use their own power, either steam, which everyone knew worked, or the in-

ternal combustion gasoline engine, about
which there was grave doubt.

General Adolphus W. Greely of the Signal Corps was probably the first military
officer who could get what we now call
R&D (Research and Development) Funds
from Congress on the strength of his imagination. In 1901–2, Congress appropri-
ated $25,000 for the Signal Corps to have
built a "flying machine for war purposes."
It was understood that the "flying machine"
would not be either a balloon or a rigid
gas bag, or dirigible, but an air-plane, a
vehicle that would move through the air as
a boat planes through water.

The director of the Smithsonian Institution, Professor Samuel P. Langley, had, as
early as 1885, said that such a vehicle was
entirely possible. In 1896 he built such a
radical device; a small unmanned model
actually flew for three-fourths of a mile
along the Potomac. He said that it would
cost $50,000 to build a full-size flying
machine. Greely turned to Congress and
the appropriation was made.

On October 7, 1903, Langley's machine,
which he called the Aerodrome A took off
from a barge in the Potomac. It struggled
for the sky, lurched, and crashed. Un-
daunted, Langley said he understood that
the crash was due to a misplaced center
of gravity, and the Aerodrome was rebuilt.
Two months later, from the same barge, the
Aerodrome A crashed exactly as it had
crashed the first time.

Congress and the press, as well, of course,
as a substantial segment of the military who
could see nothing wrong with the horse and
saber as weapons of war had hysterics at
the folly of General Greely and Professor
Langley.

The absolute idiocy of a man actually
trying to fly like a bird reached as far as
the Russian Imperial Naval Academy at
Petrograd. And with the arrogant innocence
of youth a new cadet there listened to the

Igor I. Sikorsky as a young man in Russia.
(*Sikorsky Aircraft*)

laughter of derision and decided the entire
establishment was wrong; there was no reason a man, or even hundreds of men at one
time, should not fly. But this, too, was a
practical young man, who knew the wisdom
of keeping his mouth shut, and he did. He
was Naval Cadet Igor I. Sikorsky.

On December 17, 1903, two bicycle re-
pairmen, far removed from the money of
Washington, the scientific knowledge of the
Smithsonian Institution, or even the encouragement of far-seeing officers, took their
homemade airplane to the sands of Kitty
Hawk, North Carolina, and proceeded to fly
it.

When a newspaper reporter filed the story
that Orville and Wilbur Wright's "flying
machine" had actually flown, it wasn't
printed. His editor decided that the reporter
had been at the bottle again.

But it had flown, and the world would
never be the same again.

TWO

The Signal Corps Aeronautical Division

2. Never leave the ground with the motor leaking.
7. Pilots should carry hankies in a handy position to wipe off goggles.
8. Riding on the steps, wings, or tail of a machine is prohibited.
15. Aviators will not wear spurs while flying.
20. If you see another machine near you, get out of its way.

Extracted from "Rules for Aviators," *Circa 1916.*
From *Flight Safety Foundation.*

GENERAL GREELY was replaced as Chief Signal Officer of the U. S. Army on February 9, 1906, by Brigadier General James Allen. Allen was Greely's choice for the job, and like Greely, an officer who combined foresight with a certain ability to sell the new and untried to the establishment.

He soon proved this skill. In August 1907 Allen established within the Signal Corps a formal aviation branch, known as the Aeronautical Division. He waited a few days to see what eruptions this would cause, and when they were not so high nor so severe as he thought they would be, he followed the sound military strategy that the best defense is frequently a good offense. He bearded the lions in their den.

The lions, whose bites were frequently far worse than their barks, were the members of the War Department Board of Ordnance and Fortification. Their philosophy of war was rather simple. They believed that the way to win a war was to build the strongest, largest fort possible, and equip it with the largest cannon. And then, of course, sit there.

What Allen actually said to this imposing array of staunch supporters of The Old And Tried is now buried in archives somewhere. But history records that not only did Allen talk them into the idea of buying a non-rigid gas envelope, incorrectly called a dirigible, for the Signal Corps, but further into giving him almost four times as much money as he needed. After solemn deliberation behind closed doors, the Board of Ordnance and Fortification gave General

Brigadier General James Allen, Chief Signal Officer of U. S. Army, (1906–1913). (*Defense Department*)

Captain Charles de Forest Chandler. (Photo dated February 2, 1901.) (*Signal Corps*)

Allen $25,000, in November 1907. The Signal Corps awarded a contract to Thomas S. Baldwin of $6750 to build such a vehicle.

Allen now had an Aeronautical Division, plus a new balloon under construction, plus $18,250 left of his appropriation. He next followed the well-known cavalry tactic of exploiting a weakness in the opposition.

On December 23, 1907, the Aeronautical Division of the Signal Office, Captain Charles de Forest Chandler, Officer-in-Charge, advertised for a *Heavier Than Air Flying Machine*.

The machine was to be "entirely supported by the dynamic reaction of the atmosphere, and having no gas bag." It was to be constructed so that it could be taken apart and moved about in a standard Army horse-drawn wagon. It was to be simple enough so that an "intelligent man" could become "proficient in its use within a rea-

sonable length of time" and the contract price was to include instruction of two pilots.

Technically, the machine was going to have to carry two men 125 miles without landing, and be capable of 40 miles per hour in still air. Part of its acceptance test was to be a flight of at least "one hour without touching the ground," and during which "it must be steered in all directions without difficulty and at all times under perfect control and equilibrium."

A man from Chicago by the name of J. F. Scott announced that he could build a machine meeting all these specifications for $1000, and do it within 185 days. An A. M. Herring of New York said he could build such a machine in 180 days, but it would cost the Signal Corps $20,000. The brothers Wright bid $25,000 and 200 days.

General Allen grandly informed all of

the contenders that their bid had been accepted. He put behind him, like a reformed sinner dealing with the devil, the cold fact that he didn't have the full $20,000 to accept the Herring bid, and was some $7000 shy of having the wherewithal to pay the Wright brothers should they actually build such a machine.

Not everyone in the Aeronautical Division of the Signal Office had such all-abiding faith in Aviation. Captain Chandler, soon after the specifications were announced, formally reported that one of the three enlisted men assigned to the Aeronautical Division on its birth, one Private Joseph Barrett, had never shown up in Washington and must therefore be classified a deserter.

Neither he nor Mr. Scott of the $1000 bid was ever heard from again. Mr. Herring failed to produce an airplane.

On August 18, 1908, the Baldwin non-rigid dirigible, now more accurately known as an "airship," successfully completed its trials. It looked like a plump cigar, with a gasoline engine-driven propeller hanging beneath it. Captain Chandler immediately tested the three young officers Lieutenants Frank P. Lahm, Benjamin D. Foulois, and Thomas E. Selfridge who had volunteered to serve under him, by turning them over to Baldwin for pilot training.

Two days after the airship was accepted by Chandler and Allen, the brothers Wright showed up at Fort Myer, Virginia, across the Potomac from Washington, with their airplane.

General Allen went before the Board of Ordnance and Fortifications to announce that there had been a slight miscalculation in development costs. He pointed out that he had really saved the taxpayer's money in obtaining for the Army a gasborne airship, getting it for less than seven thousand when twenty-five had been authorized, and for a little extra money, he could now provide the Army with a real flying machine.

Wincing somewhat, the Board of Ordnance and Fortification gave him the extra money he needed to pay the Wright brothers. With the money came their hope that the flying machine would really fly. And the implication that, for the future of General Allen's military career, it had better.

On September 3, 1908, the Wright brothers flew their airplane before an Army audience which included the three new balloon pilots and a delegation of officers from the Board of Ordnance and Fortifications. The plane was a modification of the Wright Model 1905. The engine and propeller were behind the pilot and passenger, and in front of them was what appeared to be another tail.

The first flight lasted seventy-one seconds. Other flights followed, and on September 9, 1908, with Orville Wright at the controls, the plane remained aloft for one hour, 135 seconds, two minutes and fifteen seconds more than the contract called for.

The Board of Ordnance and Fortifications, while not exactly beside themselves with joy and approbation for General Allen, were neither no longer preparing a resignation for his signature. The Wright machine had done what Allen had said it would do.

The next step was to be the instruction of Army officers as pilots. Before this actually began, Orville Wright took Lieutenant Selfridge up on a familiarization flight. Selfridge, generally conceded to be the most knowledgeable of the fledglings, was already technically a pilot. On May 19, 1908, he had flown, solo, the "White Wing," the airplane designed and built by the inventor of the telephone, Alexander Graham Bell.

Flying 150 feet over Fort Myer, Wright put the plane into a steep turn. The wing flexed, and the propeller snagged on a wing brace wire. The propeller blade snapped off, and the plane, out of control, crashed.

Selfridge died that afternoon, the first man killed by a heavier-than-air flying machine.

Lieutenant Frank P. Lahm (left) and Orville Wright at Fort Myer, Virginia, July 27, 1909.
(U. S. Air Force)

Orville Wright was hospitalized for several weeks with his injuries, but Wilbur immediately went to work repairing the aircraft's damage, and shifting the wing brace wires to prevent a recurrence of the accident.

They returned to Fort Myer with an improved version of the plane on June 20, 1909. On July 27, 1909, Lieutenant Lahm rode with Orville Wright in the first test flight. Lieutenant Foulois flew with Orville on the final test flight on July 30, and on August 2, the Army accepted the Wright airplane, naming it U. S. Army Aeroplane Number 1.

Lieutenant Frederick E. Humphreys took Selfridge's place in the tiny corps of Army aviators. On the afternoon of October 26, 1909, Humphreys soloed first, followed by Lahm. On November 3, 1909, the Navy appeared officially on the aviation scene when Lieutenant George C. Sweet soloed Army Aeroplane Number 1 and became the fourth military, and first naval aviator.

Early in November, Humphreys was returned to the Corps of Engineers and Lahm to the Cavalry. Foulois remained with aviation, and went with the airplane to Fort Sam Houston, Texas, for the winter. He was having some trouble landing the machine, so the Wright brothers obliged by sending him instructions by mail. When this didn't prove entirely satisfactory, they finally sent a flight instructor down to him.

For two years, the aerial might of the United States Army, Navy, and Marine Corps consisted of correspondence-school pilot Foulois and one airplane. Near Baltimore, a man by the name of Glenn Curtiss had come up with a flyable flying machine, and since the only person in the world he knew who might conceivably be interested in this was General Allen, Curtiss sought him out.

The timing of his visit to Allen was propitious. Allen had been working on the Board of Ordnance and Fortifications all the time, and had finally persuaded them to go to the Congress with an appeal for more money specifically for aviation. The $25,000 and extra-Wright brothers money had been taken from the Army's general appropriations.

The Congress surprised everybody by authorizing $125,000 at just about the time Glenn Curtiss showed up to announce he had a flying machine. Allen and Chandler went to see what he had and bought it on the spot. Curtiss was told to start making four more. Then they found three more lieutenants to be trained as pilots. They were Paul W. Beck, John C. Walker, Jr., and George E. M. Kelly. After initial training by Curtiss the three were sent to join Foulois at Fort Sam Houston.

On May 10, 1911, at Fort Sam, Kelly was killed in a crash, and became the first training fatality.

By September 1911, the Army had three balloons, five airplanes, and six young men

rated as airplane pilots. Since there was no Army Regulation defining just who a pilot should be, or what skills he must possess, the Army adopted the rules of the Aero Club of America, which in turn used those set up by the Fédération Aéronautique Internationale (FAI).

By November 1912, there were twelve airplanes in America's aerial arsenal, with a pilot for each. Thirty-nine enlisted men, several of whom became Army Air Forces general officers before retirement, had been recruited for aviation service. Three of the twelve planes were hydroplanes, capable of using the water as a runway. One of these was the Army's first "puller" aircraft, with the propeller in front.

In that month, the Army decided to see if airplanes could be used as effectively as balloons had been used in the Civil War to direct artillery fire. H. H. Arnold, a

Lieutenant Benjamin D. Foulois (in goggles, right) with an early Wright airplane. This photo, taken in New York City in the early spring of 1911, also shows (left to right) Corporal Vernon Burge, Private Brown, Ser-

geant Marcus, Sergeant Stephen J. Idsorek, Foulois, and the civilian mechanic, Oliver G. Simmons. The airplane was owned by Robert Collier, of the Collier Publishing Co.

(U. S. Army)

General of the Air Force Henry H. "Hap" Arnold, America's ranking airman during World War II, as a U. S. Army Signal Corps captain. (*Defense Department*)

bright young second lieutenant, was sent to the Field Artillery Board at Fort Riley, Kansas.

The tests were an unqualified success, and so was the second lieutenant. He learned to fly and became five-star General Henry H. "Hap" Arnold of the Army Air Forces during World War II.

In 1913, with the threat of war in Europe acknowledged by all but a wishful few, the Congress turned its attention to the United States Army. A bill was proposed in 1913 to establish an Aeronautical Branch of the Army with the same sort of importance as infantry or artillery. This was opposed by most of the aviators, and by others. It was felt that the major role of aviation would

be to deliver messages and to gather information, roles within the Signal Corps' mission. No branch liked the idea of having one more arm of service competing for congressional appropriations. On July 18, 1914, Congress created, within the Signal Corps, an Aviation Section. And then the buildup began.

In 1914, Europe went to war. On April 6, 1917, the United States joined in. Between the time the war began, and America's actual entry into it, the airplane underwent a frenzied improvement program under the impetus of combat. The first plane-to-plane combat came as something of a shock to aviators on both sides. Before the first pilot had fired his pistol at the pilot of an enemy aircraft, there had been sort of a gentleman's agreement that pilots fought the elements and technology and not each other.

Aerial pistol duels soon gave way to aerial shotgun duels, then aerial machine-gun duels, and ultimately to dual machine guns synchonized to fire between spinning propeller blades.

There was a great deal of glamour attached to World War I aviation. It tends to obscure the fact that aviation in World War I bore a much greater resemblance to what Army aviation does today, than to the Army Air Forces and its operations in World War II.

American pilots eager to fight before America declared war joined the British Royal Air Force and Royal Canadian Air Force, and formed their own squadron in the French Air Service, the Lafayette Escadrille. They formed the nucleus for the rapid expansion of American aviation once America entered the war.

Elliott White Springs, to later become president of the huge Springs Cotton Mills and good friend of Gypsy Rose Lee, gave up Princeton and his Stutz Bearcat to go to France to fly in the war to end war. Race-

Silver and embroidered World War I pilot's wings. (*Defense Department*)

self a tribute to German observation aviation, and to a realization on the part of General Pershing that prohibiting German observation of our lines, chasing their observation planes away with our pursuit planes, was nearly as important as making our own observations.

Twenty of the other twenty-one American squadrons were engaged in one form or another of aerial reconnaissance. Twelve were "Corps Observation Squadrons," assigned to Corps commanders on the ground and providing them with both aerial reconnaissance and aerial messenger service. Three squadrons were designated "Army Observation Squadrons" and performed their observation and messenger services for General Pershing's Headquarters, American Expeditionary Force.

There were five squadrons designated "Reconnaissance Squadrons" and they were assigned as needed to perform specific reconnaissance missions wherever required,

car driver Eddie Rickenbacker who went to France as a sergeant, and chauffeur to General John J. Pershing, persuaded the general to send him to flight school. He became Captain Eddie Rickenbacker, America's greatest ace, of the Hat-in-the-Ring Squadron.

The long line of attractive, bona-fide young American heroes lives on in memory a half century later. The aerial war is recalled as one of dogfights in the dawn between gallant young men of opposing armies. The function of aviation is overlooked.

Thirty-nine American squadrons fought in World War I in France. There were eighteen pursuit squadrons, which is in it-

Elliott White Springs beside his fighter plane in France, 1917. (*Defense Department*)

The Curtiss JN-4A, the "Jenny." (*U. S. Air Force*)

The De Havilland DH-4 bomber. (*U. S. Air Force*)

The first Sikorsky helicopter built in Russia in 1909. (*Sikorsky Aircraft*)

Igor Sikorsky's *The Grand*. With him in the nose is Czar Nicholas II. (*Sikorsky Aircraft*)

Sikorsky's *Ilya Murometz* S-22"B" coming in for a landing in 1914.

(Sikorsky Aircraft)

sometimes for Headquarters, AEF, sometimes for one or another of the major American units.

There was only one American bombardment squadron and it was trained and equipped to conduct operations at night. In 150 missions over German-held territory, it dropped 275,000 pounds of bombs. The same squadron reported that 1174 "targets of opportunity" were engaged by its planes during the war. This generally translated to mean that a crew took a bomber aloft and dropped their bombs on whatever German forces or fortifications they happened to see.

The primary function of aviation in the First World War was simultaneously to provide the ground commander with aerial reconnaissance (there were 6672 scheduled observation missions) and to deny the German Army aerial reconnaissance of American positions (about 13,000 "pursuit" missions were flown; the exact number can't

be determined, because a scheduled "observation" mission often turned into a "pursuit" mission on the way out or the way back). More than 17,000 aerial photographs were made of German positions and troop movements. No count was made of the number of times aviators directed artillery fire from the air.

The United States came out of World War I with a new, but substantial aviation tradition. As it rather surprised us to suddenly become a major world power, we were surprised to find that we were now on the verge of becoming the world's leading aviation power.

And American aviation genius was about to get a new recruit.

On August 18, 1911, the Imperial Aero Club of Russia which had turned, like the U. S. Army Signal Corps to the Fédération Aéronautique Internationale for its pilot standards, awarded license number 64 to Igor I. Sikorsky. The license came after the fact: Young Sikorsky had built his first helicopter (which got off the ground, but wouldn't carry a load) in 1909. A larger version, which flew at the end of a tether, but which wouldn't carry a load either, was flown in 1910.

In 1910, Sikorsky built his first airplane, which flew on the first attempt. By December 1911, Sikorsky had designed, built, and flown six different aircraft. In May 1913 he flew a twin-engined, six passenger airplane, the Grand which had dual controls, and a glass-windowed cabin complete to wicker tables and chairs for the passengers.

In 1914, he built a four-engined airplane, the *Ilya Murometz* and showed it to both Grand Duke Nicholas and Emperor Nicholas II, Czar of All the Russias, before sending it off to drop 1000-pound bombs on the Germans. It was the largest operational aircraft in any army in the World War. Later versions of the *Ilya Murometz,* the C and E models looked like the Flying Fortresses of a generation later, complete to nose and tail turrets and six- and eight-man crews.

It has been said with some justification that Igor Sikorsky's airplanes were the only efficient Russian weapons of the war.

The designer of these aircraft, and of the first flyable helicopter, was also a practical observer of politics. He knew that there was nothing for a man like him in the paradise the Soviets were about to establish in his native land. He escaped from Russia in March 1918, and went to Paris. Paris was, of course, the center of wartime aviation, but Sikorsky saw that with the end of the war approaching, so also would end French aviation.

Aviation in the United States, however, was an entirely different area. Not quite a year from his escape from the Communists, on March 30, 1919, almost penniless, Igor I. Sikorsky landed in New York City.

He got a job as a translator for the Russian Institute, and a six-dollar a week room, and lived on coffee, rolls, and Boston baked beans, which could be obtained at a Horn & Hardart Automat for fifteen cents.

At night, he began to design aircraft of all kinds, and kept returning to the one aircraft idea he really hadn't been able to make work, the rotary-winged helicopter.

On March 5, 1923, he founded the Sikorsky Aero Engineering Corporation, whose assets consisted in the main of his imagination, his determination, and what little savings he and a small band of fellow Russians immigrants could scrape up.

THREE

Could Nothing Stop the Army Air Corps?

WHEN the Congress, on July 18, 1914 created, within the Signal Corps the Aviation Section, it also created three new designations, Junior Military Aviator, Military Aviator, and Aviation Mechanic.

The first pilot's insignia weren't wings, but rather a representation of the bald eagle in flight, making a landing and clutching between his feet a sign reading *Military Aviator*. Pilot's wings came later, the stylized wings adopted from the wings of Royal Air Force.

On May 21, 1918, President Woodrow Wilson created two federal agencies, the Division of Military Aeronautics and the Bureau of Aircraft Production, and placed both under the jurisdiction of the Secretary of War. Three days later Secretary of War Newton D. Baker combined the two into the Air Service, but it wasn't until August 27, 1918, that a director was named: the Second Assistant Secretary of War was thereafter to be, ex officio, the Director of the Air Service.

Aviation was no longer a part of the Signal Corps.

On November 11, 1918, the war to end all wars came to an end. The American Expeditionary Force returned home, bringing with it two unusual and controversial brigadier generals, William "Billy" Mitchell of the Air Service, and Douglas MacArthur, who had commanded the 42nd (Rainbow) Division in France. The two men, and their wives, became friends.

Mitchell promptly began to announce that aviation, particularly bombardment aviation, was the weapon of the future. He presented this as a statement of fact, rather than a theory, and, in an attempt to both shut him up publicly and to teach him the error of his reasoning, the establishment announced a public test.

The German battleship *Ostfriesland,* in American possession, was due to be scuttled at sea. It was a magnificent vessel, and everyone knew it was unsinkable. Mitchell was offered the chance to sink it, before the eyes of not only senior Army and Navy officers but before the eyes of the newsreel cameras.

The Battleship Admirals and the Coast

Brigadier General William "Billy" Mitchell.
(*Defense Department*)

Artillery Generals gathered one sunny day in 1921 on the decks and command bridges of American vessels off the Virginia coast, and as tautly starched Marines served coffee, watched Mitchell's frail little airplane arrive over the horizon.

The topic of conversation was not so much Mitchell, who was clearly a fool and deserved the humiliation he was about to experience, but rather the questionable wisdom of scuttling the *Ostfriesland* and the other captured, or war prize, vessels. It was very much, some said, like shooting a splendid and perfectly healthy cavalry horse simply because its rider had lost the battle.

Mitchell's frail little airplanes appeared over the *Ostfriesland,* and it was said all over the command bridges that it was really insulting, in a way, to submit such a magnificent fighting vessel to this shower of pigeon droppings before sending her de-

cently, if sadly, to the bottom by scuttling.

The bombs, the pigeon droppings, fell from Mitchell's bombers. It was noticed with something like righteousness that they couldn't even hit the huge *Ostfriesland* with all of their eggs. Some of them, the admirals and the generals saw, missed the ship entirely, and exploded harmlessly in the water beside her.

The *Ostfriesland* erupted in smoke from the hits, and immediately began to settle as the near misses ruptured her below-the-water line planes. She went to the bottom before Mitchell's planes were out of sight.

There was an awkward silence for a while among the Battleship Admirals and the Coast Artillery Generals and then one admiral had a thought:

"It wasn't really fair," he said. "The *Ostfriesland* was dead in the water."

That was certainly true and then one of the Coast Artillery Generals had a thought. "Neither was she firing back," he said. "There were no anti-aircraft cannon."

This was taken up like a slogan at a civil rights meeting. And it was generally pronounced that Mitchell's sinking of the *Ostfriesland* by aerial bombardment was merely a great deal of sound and fury, signifying nothing.

Mitchell, if he had done what was expected of a member of the military, would have kept his mouth shut, let the facts— the *Ostfriesland had* gone to the bottom— speak for themselves and bide his time until he was higher up in the heirarchy, as certainly he would have been and in a position to do what he thought was necessary.

But he wasn't that kind of a man. He was as passionate in his belief that the United States must develop a strategic bombing force as he was brilliant in developing the techniques and strategy. He could, literally, see the future and it was his judgment that he would have failed his duty as an officer by keeping his mouth shut.

8:33 A.M., July 21, 1921. Bombs from Billy Mitchell's Martin Bombers miss, then strike the *Ostfriesland* amidships.

(*Defense Department*)

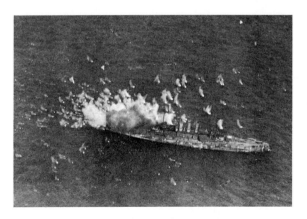

8:38 A.M., July 21, 1921. Mortally wounded, the *Ostfriesland* starts to the bottom.

(*Defense Department*)

He went to the public, which is heresy for a professional soldier, to get public support for his views. He was a good deal less than tactful in his publicly stated opinions of those in the services who opposed his views.

He was finally, in 1925, and with great reluctance on the part of a military establishment who didn't want to air their dirty linen in public, brought before a court-martial. He had been told to keep his mouth shut; he had not kept his mouth shut. He was charged with conduct unbecoming an officer and a gentleman.

His defense counsel was a member of the Congress; his good friend General Douglas MacArthur was a member of the court. Mrs. Mitchell and Mrs. MacArthur came to the court-martial together every day. The Billy Mitchell case was on the front page of every newspaper in the country.

He was found to be guilty as charged. Reduced to the rank of colonel, denied the privilege of command and put on reduced pay, eventually he resigned from the army in 1926.

His disciples, a courageous far-seeing handful, offered to resign their commissions themselves. He talked them out of it and men like H. H. Arnold stayed in uniform to command the vast aerial army of the World War II.

Mitchell's ideas were sound and the Congress and even some senior Army officers saw this. In 1926, the Army asked for, and the Congress provided, statutory authority for the Army Air Corps, together with a new position, Assistant Secretary of War for Air.

The Battleship Admirals and the Coast Artillery Generals were still firmly in control of the military establishment, but there was a crack in their plates and fortifications. None of the junior officers, either Air Corps or Navy, really believed the Army-Navy Board, General of the Armies John J. Pershing, presiding, when it said, "the battleship would continue as the bulwark of the nation's defenses."

On July 17, 1935, the 15-ton Boeing Model 299, later to be the B-17 Flying Fortress," the largest land plane ever built in the United States, made its maiden flight in Seattle.

The key word in that sentence is *land*

plane. Igor I. Sikorsky had built seaplanes larger than the Model 299 long before Boeing got around to it. By searching through junk yards for usable components, and by devoting a substantial part of his imagination to borrowing more money, Sikorsky was able to make a successful flight of the twin-engine, 14-passenger 115-mph S-29A on September 25, 1924.

The vice-president of Sikorsky at that time was a man who freely admitted an awesome lack of knowledge of aviation. He knew only that Sikorsky was a man of his word, a fellow Russian, and that he was having more trouble making money in this new land of America than he, Sergei Rachmaninoff, pianist and composer, was having. He advanced Sikorsky $5000 and began to use his prestige among the rich in Sikorsky's behalf.

On May 21, 1927, a tall, rather taciturn young Air Corps officer got inside a single engined airplane on Long Island, advanced the throttle, crossed his fingers, and took off. When his wheels touched ground again, Charles Augustus Lindbergh was in Paris, and the world had a hero whose fame has never faded.

Lindbergh's flight gave long-distance aviation a big push. People could now see a commercial future for aviation. There was still a very large amount of romance to planes and pilots, but in board rooms, solemn men were solemnly deciding that aviation was about to become commercially respectable. Sikorsky was able to get money in large amounts.

In January 1931, he personally flew as part of the crew of a Sikorsky S-38, a twin-engined 8-passenger amphibian, from Bridgeport to Panama. From there another Russian refugee, Captain Boris Sergievsky, flew the S-38 onto Chile.

In October 1931, the four-engined, Sikorsky designed and built Pan American Airways' S-40. Christened the *American Clipper* by Mrs. Herbert Hoover, it made its maiden flight with Colonel Charles Lindbergh at the controls. Its maiden commercial flight, with Lindbergh again flying and a full load of paying passengers, was between Miami and the Panama Canal Zone.

A larger version of the S-40, the S-42, capable of carrying a payload of 4400 pounds more than 1200 miles followed and

The Sikorsky S-29-A. (*Sikorsky Aircraft*)

The Sikorsky S-42. (*Sikorsky Aircraft*)

was promptly put into service by Pan American. On April 17, 1935, three months to the day before the B-17 was first flown in Seattle, the just as heavy Sikorsky S-42 took off from Alameda, California, for Hawaii with a crew of six and a load of mail. The flight was uneventful. Passenger flights followed immediately, as far as New Zealand. The same month the B-17 first flew, Pan American began the first regularly scheduled flights across the Atlantic, using the Sikorsky S-42 *Clipper*.

The era of the big plane had arrived. Great effort was being made to make planes bigger and faster and to give them longer range. Hardly anyone at all paid attention to the other end of the picture, Mr. Piper and his Piper Cub, a two-passenger puddle-jumper which could be flown practically from your back yard, using a tiny little engine and with navigation instruments limited to compass, vertical position ball, and airspeed indicator.

Within the Army, a General Headquarters, Air Force, was established in March of 1935, and placed in command of tactical units and reported, in turn, directly to the General Staff. This proved an impractical arrangement and in 1939, with the first swell of our military building up, GHQ Air Force was placed under the command of the Chief of Air Corps.

On June 20, 1941, the Army Air Forces was created by the Congress. Its position was clarified shortly after the war began when, on March 9, 1942, the War Department established three co-equal commands: the Army Air Forces, the Army Ground Forces, and the Army Service Forces.

The Army Air Forces were charged with providing the Army with whatever support it needed. It was the Air Forces judgment that what the Army needed was bombers, to strike at the enemy in his rear areas and his factories. The Army and the nation would need protection against enemy bombers and fighter planes were developed to provide this sort of protection. The Army would need aircraft to drop its paratroops and the Air Forces made provision to provide transport aircraft squadrons and even to provide a rudimentary aerial supply system for supplies and personnel.

The Air Forces emphasis was on large,

long-range bombers and transports, and on fast, high-flying heavily armed fighters. Hardly any attention at all was paid to a small group of Army officers who cried plantively that it was going to be impossible to direct artillery fire from a B-17, no matter what a splendid Flying Fortress that aircraft was, or to carry messages between infantry regiments in P-39s and P-40s, because those splendid, high-speed machines could not land in a cornfield or on a country road.

Control of aircraft was another sore point. The Air Forces, having just been granted a large degree of autonomy, was simply unwilling to place its aircraft under the orders of a Ground Forces officer. Their position was like that of the Navy. The Army could make its desires known and every effort would be made to satisfy them, in the Air Forces' methods, techniques, and good time. Otherwise, said the Air Forces, there seemed to be little sense in having autonomy.

If the Army said it needed observation planes, the Air Forces would provide observation squadrons and it did. But it either bristled with indignation or maintained a stony silence when the Army said that the planes provided weren't what was needed, that they were too fast, that they were too difficult to maintain, that there weren't enough of them, and that they required too elaborate airfield facilities.

In the summer of 1940, the summer that would see the first massive American maneuvers ever held, a lieutenant in the tradition of "Gatling Gun" Parker decided that since no one else seemed to be willing or able to do anything about what was to him an obvious problem with an equally obvious solution, he would do it himself.

Lieutenant Thomas McCord Watson, Jr., an artilleryman, called the Piper Aircraft Company and announced he wanted to discuss the role of light aircraft in direct-

ing artillery fire and to serve as liaison craft.

Piper's president, William T. Piper, Sr., dispatched a Piper Cub and a salesman pilot named Tom Case from New Orleans to Camp Beauregard, Louisiana, in August 1940. The ship had no radios and they communicated with the ground exactly as Professor Lowe had communicated with the forces of the Army of the Potomac from the balloon *Enterprise*. They wrapped their messages around something heavy and dropped them out the window.

The effectiveness of the one lonely Cub made an impression on Lieutenant Watson, who began preaching the gospel of light aviation to his superiors, meeting some success, and on salesman Case, who realized that since the idea was perfectly valid, it meant Piper Cub could sell large numbers of its airplanes to the Army.

At almost the opposite end of the rank structure, a Cavalryman turned Tanker,

Brigadier General Adna R. Chaffee, USA.
(U. S. Army)

Brigadier General Adna R. Chaffee, was having some thoughts of his own about light airplanes. He already had begun to see that one of the problems of armor, or tanks, was that, splendid weapons of war though they might be, they had an already demonstrated propensity for causing traffic jams of heroic proportions.

The German Panzer Blitzkrieg into Poland and France would have had even more Blitz if its tank columns had known where they were going and how to get there most quickly.

Chaffee well knew that despite all the press agents' and war correspondents' glowing stories, the tank was not perfect. To get across a river more than five feet in depth, for example, it needed a bridge. If there was no bridge, the tanks simply couldn't get across. The Germans had found that out in both France and Poland. A literally irresistible tank column would race up to a river, find the bridge blown, and then spend hours . . . or even days . . . first looking for a suitable bridge across the river, and then getting to it.

General Chaffee knew that the present alternative to that, either fast-moving light tanks, or unarmed motorcycle or jeep reconnaissance to get to bridges and other natural or man-made obstacles first, was both slow and not necessarily effective. He reasoned that a light plane preceding the column could not only find out that a bridge had been blown much sooner than even the most daredevil motorcyclist, but could get the word back to an advancing tank column commander much sooner. Further, since a light-plane-borne observer could spot a destroyed bridge, he could also spot a usable bridge, and redirect a tank column.

He could also fly around locating the tank columns themselves; although it wasn't generally considered polite to mention it, it was often necessary to tell tank column commanders where they were.

Chaffee made it a blunt statement: The Army needed its own light aircraft, and the sooner they got them, the better. He went on record as wholly supporting the artillery in their request for what they called "organic aviation."

Not only were the aircraft being designed and built to go as high and as fast as possible, which made them, in direct proportion to speed and altitude, less useful to the ground army, but the Air Forces and the Ground Forces had developed what the psychologists call a "personality clash."

The Air Forces which had just won its lengthy and by no means bloodless fight for relative independence, was not going to place either its airplanes or any of its officers and men under Ground Forces . . . which they were already beginning to call "Army" . . . control. Without such control, reasoned the Army, they couldn't order the pilots and their planes to go where they were needed, and when.

In early June 1941 the United States Second Army, under command of Lieutenant General Ben Lear, held a week-long manuever, during which a dozen light airplanes on loan to the Army were used to direct artillery fire. The Army controlled light planes were used for the same purposes as the Air Forces controlled light aircraft theoretically at the beck and call of the Army commanders. The results were both predictable and positive: The planes under the actual control of the Army were available when and where needed. The Air Forces controlled aircraft generally arrived late, and at the wrong place.

One of the recommendations made to the War Department as a result of the Second Army manuevers was that light aircraft be assigned to artillery battalions. In July 1941 the point was proved again by the manuevers at Fort Bliss, Texas. Henry S. Wann, a Piper employee, arrived at the tent of Major General Innis P. Swift, commanding the 1st Cavalry Division. He told the somewhat surprised Swift that he had been told to make himself useful. The general asked him to share his lunch and as they were eating, a radiogram reached Swift telling him that he was about to receive an airplane for use as he saw fit.

That same day, Swift gave light aircraft the name most commonly applied to them throughout World War II. After Wann had flown Swift's aide-de-camp on an errand, the general decided he wanted the airplane himself. He sent a radio message blunt and to the point: SEND THE GRASSHOPPER. SWIFT.

In August 1941 the Third Army held manuevers in Louisiana. The Chief of Staff of Third Army, a balding, chain-smoking lieutenant colonel sought out J. M. Helbert, another Piper civilian pilot on loan to the Army, and told him he'd been up to his ears in paper all day and would be very grateful if he could fly a little.

Helbert, whose orders had been to fly anyone anywhere, waved him into his Cub. The lieutenant colonel said he'd acquired 600 hours of flight time and that he'd learned to fly in the Philippines, where he had been on the staff of General Douglas MacArthur. Helbert confessed later he had had a hard time remembering the officer's name. It was rather uncommon: D. D. Eisenhower.

During the same manuevers, Major General George S. Patton, Jr., tried Chaffee's theory of tank column direction from the air and became converted.

On December 7, 1941, the Japanese attacked the Naval Base at Pearl Harbor and virtually crippled American naval power in the Pacific. The Japanese plan of attack followed almost exactly a "hypothetical attack" of an imaginary enemy described by Brigadier General Billy Mitchell twenty years before.

It was some time before the Americans could mount an attack on the Japanese homeland. But finally, in 1942, Lieutenant Colonel (later Lieutenant General) Jimmy Doolittle, one of the officers whom Mitchell had talked out of resigning from the service in protest at his court-martial and conviction, led a flight of bombers from an aircraft carrier over the Japanese home islands. It seemed very appropriate that the bombers, B-25s, were named Mitchells after General Billy Mitchell.

In January 1942, with the United States at war, a formal test of organic field artillery aviation was ordered by the War Department. The 2nd Infantry Division and the 13th Field Artillery Brigade were named as test units. The Army Air Forces turned over to the Artillery School at Fort Sill, Oklahoma, twenty-four olive drab J-3 Piper Cubs officially known as YO-59s.

Lieutenant Colonel William W. Ford, a Regular Artillery officer, was named Director of Flight Training. Under him were eight civilian flight instructors, and a civilian in charge of aircraft maintenance. Fourteen officers were assigned as student pilots, all volunteers who had had flight experience as civilians. Only one of these was a Regular officer, West Pointer First Lieutenant Robert R. Williams.

The group was headed by Major Gordon J. Wolf, a reservist. It included one captain, four first lieutenants (including Williams), and eight second lieutenants. Four sergeants, four corporals, two pfc's, and ten buck privates, also began pilot training.

Together, they trained, and together they made their point. Army-owned, Army-controlled, light aircraft belonged in the Army. On June 6, 1942, the War Department made it official. There would be in each field artillery battalion in the Army, two light aircraft and the pilots for them. Additionally, there would be two light planes in Division Artillery Headquarters, and in the headquarters of a field artillery brigade.

Two sentences from the official memorandum authorizing Army aviation make clear how it was regarded by the higher echelons of the Army:

"Personnel are authorized at the rate of one pilot and ½ mechanic per liaison airplane."

"The airplanes will be commercial low performance aircraft on the 'Piper Cub' type."

Now that the advocates of light aircraft had convinced the brass of the value of Army aviation, it now remained to convince the Army as a whole.

FOUR

Army Aviation

THE first pilots were those with civilian flight training. The supply of these soon dried up, and the call went out for volunteers. In the early days of World War II, most of the officer corps were products of the Reserve Officer Training Corps. Most of the artillery lieutenants asked to volunteer for flight training were no more than a year or two from the fraternity house.

With the exception of Lieutenant Williams, who was, after all, a West Pointer, there was deep-seated skylarking among the new aviators. Most had volunteered for aviation because it looked like more fun than laying in field artillery pieces.

In England, where an unofficial pilot school had been set up, Lieutenant Colonel (Ret.) Lawrence Ballantine (then an ROTC lieutenant fresh from Seton Hall) was reprimanded for making the Army "aware" of Army aviation, by rolling the wheels of his Cub over the cabs of GI trucks on the move and for bombing marching columns with two-pound sacks of flour.

Army Aviation went to war in the North African invasion, and with something less than perfection. Four pilots were ordered to the USS *Ranger,* an aircraft carrier, where they found three Piper J-4s. Their orders were to fly them off the *Ranger* during the invasion, and to report for duty to the Artillery Commander, 3rd Infantry Division.

The planes were unflyable when they found them, and the four pilots, Captains Ford E. Allcorn and Brenton A. Devol, Jr., and Lieutenants John R. Shell and William Butler, had to spend most of the trip across the Atlantic working on them.

On November 8, 1942, they took off from the carrier's deck sixty miles at sea. With the carrier's speed of 25-knots added to a 35-knot wind, the Cubs were airborne as soon as the ground crew let go of their wings. One pilot reported that when he took off, the *Ranger* moved out from under him.

Three miles from shore, the tiny formation of tiny craft saw the USS *Brooklyn.* The *Brooklyn* saw them, too, and opened fire. This served as an inspiration to the rest of the ships in the 200-ship invasion fleet, and they all opened fire.

Lieutenant Lawrence Ballantine at an Army
Aviation demonstration at Tidworth, England,
in 1943. (*Courtesy Col. Ballantine*)

Butler and Devol headed up the coast,
where they landed near a French fort and
were promptly arrested as prisoners of war.
Allcorn flew along the coast, under fire from
the American ships at sea, and from the
French on shore. Three or four miles from
Fedala, his destination, Ford was taken under fire by the 2nd Armored Division, already ashore, whose marksmanship was
better than that of the Navy and the
French. Allcorn was wounded in the leg,
and the Cub caught fire. He made a crash
landing, crawled away from the burning
ship, and watched as it exploded.

But there were other light aircraft in the
holds of the invasion fleet, and other pilots,
and by the time the North African campaign was over, Army Aviation was as much
a part of the field army as the jeep.

The light planes were all known as Grasshoppers, but they weren't all Piper Cubs,

An L-4 (J-3) taking off from the USS *Ranger* in the invasion of North Africa.
(*U. S. Army Aviation Museum*)

and officially, they weren't all Grasshoppers. The first liaison aircraft, the Vultee L-1, was bought and used by the Army Air Forces who maintained liaison squadrons throughout World War II. The Air Forces bought a total of 352 of these 295-hp. two-seater aircraft.

The L-2, officially a Grasshopper, was a two-place Taylorcraft, powered by a 65-horsepower engine. There were thirteen versions of this aircraft, with the major difference between them side-by-side or tandem seating. The L-2L model was an experimental ship with a 50-hp. engine. Purchased between 1942 and 1943, there were, all told, 1949 L-2's.

The L-3 was the Aeronca Challenger, a two-seater Grasshopper with a 65-hp. engine. A crash program to provide light planes for the Army saw 1465 L-3s, in ten different models, purchased during 1942, the only year they were purchased.

The L-4 was the Piper Cub. As the Grasshopper, in ten different models, the bulk of them with 65-hp. engines, but with engines rated as high as 100-hp. being delivered, 5671 wore olive drab.

General Mark W. Clark, Commander of the Fifth Army in Italy, became an early convert to Army Aviation. While it was true that there wasn't much to any of the Grasshoppers but a tiny engine, a wooden propeller and a canvas-covered aluminum frame, it was equally true that a thirty-minute hop in a Grasshopper took its passenger just as far as a four- or five-hour ride over dusty, bumpy roads in a jeep.

Moreover, it gave its passenger a view of the terrain he could get in no other way. In the early days, because of the shortage of aircraft, the standard Army practice of the General Staff briefing the commander on the situation at the front was reversed. Because he alone had been able to get into a Cub for a look, the general wound up briefing his staff.

Clark also had the power—and was perfectly willing—to sign priority requisitions for more aircraft, and for more pilots, to be delivered as soon as possible. Clark was himself an innovator. After first claiming one of the Grasshoppers for his own, he installed a loudspeaker in it, directing his troops from the air, and simultaneously suggesting to the Arabs that the time had come to mend their sinful ways: God himself was speaking from the heavens.

By the time the invasion of Sicily was planned, Army Aviation was no longer the orphan child begging at the tent flap for support. Captain Devol, who had nearly been shot down during the North African invasion, and later released from French captivity, was given an LST (Landing Ship, Tank) to haul light airplanes in the invasion.

Devol went further than this. In thirty-six hours, he made his LST into an aircraft carrier. Right down the center of the flat-bottomed craft he built a 70-yard runway of timbers topped with pierced steel planking. On either side of the runway, their noses hanging over the side, he stored two Grasshoppers. At the end of his makeshift runway, he improvised a parking apron for four more aircraft.

When the invasion started, the LST headed into the wind, and, engines roaring, steamed at a full speed of 9 knots. Given a wind of 10 knots or better, this was enough for the little planes to stagger into the air.

And going into Sicily, only the Germans shot at them; the Americans now knew what they were.

The Germans quickly learned that the Grasshopper was more than an American toy. Fighter planes were diverted from the interception of American bombers, and from the strafing of troops, and assigned full time to shooting down the Grasshoppers. It made good sense: If a Grasshopper wasn't engaged in directing artillery fire, then the odds were it was carrying couriers,

The Army Corps' Vultee L-1. (*U. S. Air Force*)

The Taylorcraft L-2. (*U. S. Army*)

The L-3, the Aeronca "Challenger." (*U. S. Army*)

The L-4 (Piper Cub). (*U. S. Army*)

or senior officers on liaison or observation missions. Shooting down a Grasshopper meant destroying an observation post, certainly worth a fighter's attention, or eliminating a senior officer, a task worthy of a flight of Messerschmitts.

Shooting Grasshoppers down proved to be easier in theory than in practice. The little planes began flying in pairs, one serving as a watchdog for the plane doing the observing, or artillery direction. The fighters would swoop in out of the sun, in the best fighter pilot tradition. When they spotted the Grasshopper, they would open up with their battery of machine guns.

At that point, the Grasshopper pilot would stand his tiny plane on its wing, and head in the opposite direction. The fighter was going too fast to make any turn at all. If he was lucky, he simply lost his target. If he was unlucky, or careless, he flew his fighter into the ground.

When the Germans tried to counter this technique by flying low and slow, often going to the extreme of lowering their wheels and flaps to serve as air brakes, they themselves became not only vulnerable to stalls and crashes, because the planes weren't designed for that kind of flight, but to American ground fire as well.

With enthusiasm, the Grasshoppers entered the Italian campaign. General Clark turned over the Fifth Army to Lieutenant General Lucian K. Truscott when he assumed command of the 15th Army Group. Truscott's pilot was an artillery officer, Captain Jack Marinelli.

To provide Truscott with an airstrip near his headquarters in the mountainous area around La Futa Pass, Marinelli supervised the construction of a 735-foot strip whose lower end was 97-feet beneath its upper end. In U. S. Army Engineer parlance, the strip had a 20 percent gradient. At the lower end of the strip, there was a sheer drop of 2000 feet to the valley floor beneath. It was necessary to use full throttle to taxi up the runway.

On October 4, 1943, General Clark astonished the normally unshockable Neapolitans by landing on Naples' Carragiola Boulevard in a Grasshopper, getting out, and

Fifth Army Aviators, November 8, 1944. (Left to right seated Maj. F. E. Allcorn, Maj. S. A. Williamson, Lt. Col. J. T. Walker, Maj. J. L. Marinelli, Maj. J. W. Oswalt. Standing are Lt. R. E. Swisher, Capts. T. O. Morrell, T. W. Childs, J. L. Fish, V. C. Krogg and C. E. Baire. (*U. S. Army*)

The Feisler "Storche" carrying French Insignia.
(*Collection Col. L. Ballantine*)

calmly requisitioning the first GI jeep that drove by to take him to a conference.

During the battle at Anzio Beachhead, Captain John W. Oswalt directed an artillery barrage to satisfy the wildest dreams of a young artillery officer. A total of 370 cannon, in field artillery batteries on shore, and on the heavy cruisers USS *Brooklyn,* HMS *Dido,* and HMS *Orion* off Anzio responded as one gunner to Oswalt's order to "fire for effect."

During the invasion of Normandy in June 1944, Army aircraft were flown directly from England, or dismantled and trucked in. On D-Day + 1, Grasshoppers were directing artillery fire. After the breakout, and during the slashing movements of American tank columns, General Chaffee's theories of the value of the small craft in column direction were proved beyond question.

Chaffee's protégé, by now Lieutenant General George S. Patton, Jr., decided that the Grasshoppers possessed a logistics function no one else, especially the Germans, had considered. He secretly gathered almost a hundred light Army aircraft, and determined that with them he could airlift, one soldier at a time, an entire infantry battalion across the Rhine. The capture of the Remagen Bridge intact made this move un-

necessary, but the idea for movement of Army troops by their own light aircraft was Patton's.

Patton himself almost lost his life while a passenger in an L-4 near Munich. He was attacked by a Polish-flown RAF Spitfire. The plane made three passes, missing on the first two and crashing on the third.

Few aircraft of the type used by the Americans were used by the Germans, a fact historians credit to Field Marshal Hermann Göring's unwillingness to place his Luftwaffe under Wehrmacht control. The Germans had a perfectly satisfactory light aircraft, the Feisler Storch. Just before Hitler committed suicide in his Führerbunker in Berlin, Hanna Reitsch flew a Storch into the burning city, landing on the Unter den Linden, under Russian artillery and small arms fire, and with the intention of sneaking Hitler out of the city.

Hitler refused to go. Fräulein Reitsch flew out alone and lived to be received at the White House by President John F. Kennedy as an aviation pioneer. The French, claiming them as war booty, used Storches for many years after World War II.

In the Pacific, the vast distances between the islands on which the war was fought limited the use of light Army aircraft somewhat. They were used in the Philippine campaign, when MacArthur made good his "I will return" promise, and elsewhere.

In the Pacific, too, ingenuity outside of Army channels reached massive proportions. Lieutenant James Brodie came up with a cable takeoff device permitting the use of the Grasshoppers without a runway. Four steel masts suspended a cable fifty feet or so off the ground. An L-4 was fitted into a cradle and hauled close to the cable. The pilot wound up his engine and then slid along the cable until he reached flying speed, then unhooked his plane from the cradle. The device was so successful that an LST was assigned to the device, officially

An L-4 suspended on "Brodie system" cables.
(*U. S. Army Aviation Museum*)

named the USS *Brodie,* and used in the Okinawa campaign.

General Joseph W. "Vinegar Joe" Stilwell was another early convert to the Grasshopper, and typically chose an enlisted man, Staff Sergeant Lyle White, as his personal pilot. Stilwell's son-in-law, Colonel Ernest F. Easterbrook, first encountered light planes when he saw how they were used to support Merrill's Marauders in Burma. Easterbrook, after the Korean War, became an Army aviator himself and once commanded the Army Aviation Center at Fort Rucker, Alabama.

With peace came the almost instant cutback in all Army forces, including aviation. Most Army aviators got out of the service. Of those remaining, only a few competent officers were willing to stake their careers on what much of the Army still regarded as something pretty frivolous.

Enlisted pilots were phased out of the aviation program. The training program was cut back at the small pilot school at Fort Sill, Oklahoma.

In the bustle of the war, and the concern of the professional soldiers to salvage something for the Army from the economy drives that came with peace, perhaps the most significant development of all went practically unnoticed.

Igor Sikorsky had put off, not abandoned, his idea of a helicopter back in Russia, back in 1910. The *idea,* he knew, was sound. It was just that technology had not caught up with his theoretical inventiveness. Twenty years later, in 1930, now an American engineer of growing reputation, Sikorsky applied for patents on several techniques of rotary wing flight.

In 1938, with war to him inevitable, he had returned to the nuts-and-bolts development of a direct lift aircraft. By November 1939, while France and Germany were glowering at each other in the Phony War the Sikorsky VS-300 could stay in the air for two minutes. On April 15, 1941, a Sikorsky helicopter, a modified VS-300, flew for more than an hour. Two days later, mounted on floats, it took off from water. On May 6, 1941, it set a world endurance record of 1 hour, 32 minutes, 26.1 seconds. This was enough to convince the Army Air Forces that there was enough of an idea in rotary wing aircraft to merit an injection of the taxpayer's dollars.

Sikorsky was given a contract to build an experimental two-man helicopter. On the delivery flight from Connecticut to the Testing Base at Dayton, Ohio (now the Wright-Patterson Air Development Center), Igor Sikorsky, now a rather stocky, mustachioed gentleman wearing a hat with its brim up all the way around flew as co-pilot. Air Forces Colonel Frank Gregory posed for a

The maiden flight of the VS-300. Igor I. Sikorsky at the controls.

(*Sikorsky Aircraft*)

A modified (longer) VS-300. This flew for 120 seconds. (*Sikorsky Aircraft*)

Igor I. Sikorsky delivers the first U.S. military helicopter to the Army Air Forces. Orville Wright is in the middle and right is Air Forces Colonel Frank Gregory. (*United Aircraft*)

photograph to mark the delivery, on May 6, 1942, of the first helicopter by Igor I. Sikorsky. The third man in the picture, wearing a rakish hat and a broad smile is a former bicycle mechanic named Orville Wright.

It was a momentous occasion in world history. It got less space in the newspapers than publicity photographs of a jeep bouncing through the air, and nowhere near so much space as free glossy pictures of Lana Turner's upturned legs.

FIVE

Rotary Wings

It would be right to state that in the summer of 1942, the helicopter became a reality in the United States. From then on, it became a question of improving the details.

IGOR I. SIKORSKY, *"The Winged S."*

SIKORSKY had abandoned the construction of a helicopter long before World War I not because he questioned his theories of a rotary wing, but because he knew that the aviation technology available to him, especially aircraft engines, was simply too primitive to result, then, in a successful helicopter. His genius, in other words, had to wait for technology to catch up with it.

An airplane wing, or a helicopter rotor, gets its lift from the density of the atmosphere. All aerodynamic aircraft have a *ceiling,* that point at which its airfoil will no longer support the machine. Since the atmosphere is made up of gas, and since temperature and moisture content affects the density of gases, this is not a constant because temperatures and moisture content at a given altitude vary.

An air*foil* is necessary for the flight of any aerodynamic vehicle, either air*plane* or helicopter, both of which are air*craft*. The word helicopter, incidentally, goes back to 1872, and means "spiral wing."

An airfoil is any surface designed to produce a lifting effect when air is passed over it. An airplane's airfoil is a wing; a helicopter's airfoil is a rotor, or, almost as commonly and certainly more precisely, a rotary wing.

From a point at the front of the midsection of a given airfoil to a point at the midsection of the trailing edge, the air must travel a greater distance over the top surface of the foil than over the under surface. This produces a force known as *lift;* one third of it coming from the upward impact of air on the under surface, and two-thirds from the lowered pressure area on the upper surface of the wing. At a given speed through a given atmospheric density an airfoil of a given surface will lift itself, and

Stanley Hiller, at the controls of his counter-rotating rotor helicopter moments before it crashed. (*Fairchild-Hiller*)

its aircraft off the earth, and suspend it aerodynamically in flight.

This theory is by no means new. But it had to wait for the Wright brothers and Igor Sikorsky to translate the physicist's theory into a practical tool of man.

The Wrights took an airfoil and an airscrew, or propeller, and combined them to attain flight. The airscrew, exactly as a propeller on a boat, pushed the aircraft, and its airfoil, through the air. On the beach at Kitty Hawk, they pushed it fast enough through the air for the forces of lift to overcome the forces of drag, and it became airborne.

But it required a takeoff run, and a landing run, a transitional phase between groundborne and airborne. As aircraft grew larger, and heavier, they required larger wings to get them airborne, larger engines, and longer takeoff and landing rolls. Runways today of two and three miles in length are common.

The first idea of an aircraft which would not need a runway came naturally and easily. If it were possible to push a machine through the air horizontally, then it should be possible to pull one up through the air vertically.

As a theory, it was sound. As a practical matter it was considerably more difficult.

First of all, it required a tremendous amount of power, Sikorsky's early problems were as much a lack of power as anything else. And secondly, it got involved with a law of physics, and it is impossible to appeal to a higher court for reversal of Newton's third law.

"For every action," theorized Sir Isaac, "there is an equal and opposite reaction."

The word is torque. As the propeller of an airplane turns in one direction, torque is applied in the other direction. But the wings of an airplane, in addition to providing lift, serve to counteract this countertwisting effect. It is much easier to push the propeller through the air than it is to spin the wings in the opposite direction. While torque is a bona-fide consideration in fixed-wing flight, it's seldom really troublesome.

But with a helicopter, the reverse was true. As the engine tried to spin the rotary wings in one direction, Newton's third law tried to spin the rest of the machine in the opposite direction.

When Sikorsky examined this problem, he determined that a countertorque airscrew was required. "Tail rotors," three small propellers, two horizontal and one vertical, mounted on the end of a boom outside the arc of the main rotor solved the problem.

When Stanley Hiller, the young California genius, designed his first helicopter at the age of nineteen, his first solution was to have counterrotating rotor blades on the same shaft. This was a sound idea, and was later used successfully by others. Hiller's counterrotating rotor machine failed however. Hiller next tried a single rotor aircraft with a countertorque device consisting of an air duct, blowing exhaust fumes and compressed air against the atmosphere at the tail of the helicopter. This, too, proved technically impractical, and finally Hiller followed Sikorsky's idea of a vertically mounted countertorque propeller in his first successful machine.

Frank Piasecki, the Philadelphia helicopter inventor, decided he could overcome the torque problem by using two main rotors,

instead of one, and having them rotate in opposite directions. This worked, too. And finally, helicopters have been designed and built using jet engines at the extreme tip of the main rotor blades. Since the "equal and opposite reaction" to the force making the blade move through the air is against the atmosphere, it doesn't have any effect on the machine itself.

But these developments came later. In the beginning was Sikorsky, with his one lifting rotor and one countertorque rotor.

The first problem to overcome was developing an engine powerful enough to turn a rotary wing through the air with enough force to gain the necessary lift to pick itself, the airframe and the engine off the ground. The evolution of the internal combustion gasoline engine provided this power. The engine in Sikorsky's first successful helicopter sounds as if it would have fit into a Volkswagen. It was air-cooled, four-cylinder, and produced a mighty 75-hp.

This was enough to turn the 28-foot, three-bladed main rotary wing, the three-tail propellers, or rotors, and to give them the lift necessary to haul a welded steel frame, a two-wheel landing gear, and Igor I. Sikorsky himself into the air, vertically.

Sikorsky soon learned that only one tail rotor, mounted vertically, and controllable by pilot's foot pedals, in the same place, and used in the same way as airplane rudder pedals, was enough. The outrigger, downdraft tail rotors were discarded.

Other forces apply to rotary wing aircraft, now presented as simply statements of fact to helicopter student pilots, but which Sikorsky and the others literally had to find out for themselves, generally by experiment with themselves offered as the guinea pigs.

How to move a rotary wing through the air was the first problem. It was obvious that a horizontally mounted airscrew would have to be larger than a propeller designed to pull, rather than lift.

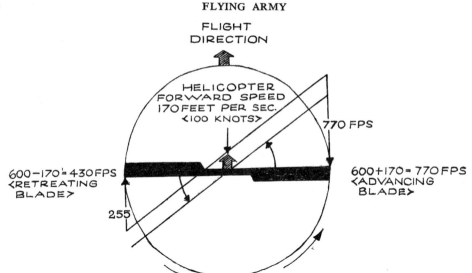

FLIGHT
DIRECTION

HELICOPTER
FORWARD SPEED
170 FEET PER SEC.
<100 KNOTS>

770 FPS

600−170=430FPS
<RETREATING
BLADE>

600+170=770FPS
<ADVANCING
BLADE>

255

600 FEET PER SECOND

<ROTATIONAL VELOCITY>±<HEL FORWARD SPEED>=<AIRSPEED OF BLADE>

Rotational velocity of a rotary wing. (*Emma J. Butterworth*)

Size itself became an almost immediate problem. No longer was revolutions per minute going to be the sole consideration. As the length of rotor blades grew, so did the tip speed. This wasn't much of a problem for aircraft propellers because on even huge airplanes, the propeller arc, the radius between the center of the propeller and the extreme tip seldom exceeded 10 feet. Sikorsky's first rotor blade had a radius of 14 feet, and they went up in size from there.

In addition to the centrifugal forces attempting to tear the blade and its hub apart, the tip speed of the blade itself began to approach the speed of sound, and that meant buffeting easily capable (at the sound barrier) of destroying the blade, the engine and the entire aircraft.

By experimentation, they found that, as a general rule, tip speed of a helicopter rotor should not exceed 600 feet per second during normal takeoff. This permitted a safety factor (speed could be increased in an emergency and still not reach the speed of sound) and seemed to provide the necessary lift at the least possible strain on the rotor hub.

As the machines staggered hesitantly into the air, other facts of physical life, interesting on paper, came to life, and shook some helicopters to death, and crashed others.

They found, for example, that because the body of the helicopter, containing the pilot, the engine, and the fuel was heavier, and necessarily hanging below the rotor blades, the whole thing, when airborne, turned into a pendulum, with the fuselage swinging below the rotor just like the shiny weight on a grandfather's clock.

There's never been a solution to this problem. Pilots have had to learn techniques which reduce the tendency of the helicopter to become a pendulum, and maneuvers which will stop the movement if it begins.

And as the helicopter assumed some of the characteristics of a clock pendulum, it also had to cope with the characteristics of a gyroscope, specifically *gyroscopic precession*.

Any rotating body, from the earth itself to a child's toy gyroscope, behaves in a

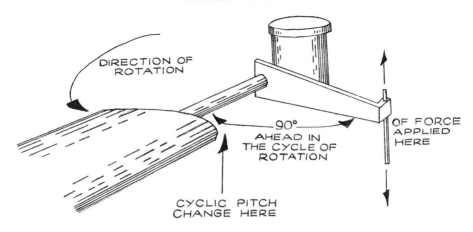

DIRECTION OF
ROTATION

90°
AHEAD IN
THE CYCLE OF
ROTATION

OF FORCE
APPLIED
HERE

CYCLIC PITCH
CHANGE HERE

The forces of precession applied to a rotary wing. (*Emma J. Butterworth*)

peculiar manner when force is applied to it. The effect of the force applied is manifest 90° in the direction of rotation from the point where force is applied. As they rocketed back from the moon, our astronauts gave the world a demonstration of this on television.

As applied to the rotary wing of a helicopter, evisioned as a disc rotating counterclockwise, force intended to push the forward end of the disc down, necessary for forward movement, would instead tilt the disc down to the left, 90° from the point of applied force.

This problem has been solved simply and quickly, by installing into the helicopter directional controls 90° out of phase. The pilot has the sensation that he is applying force where he wants it, to move the rotor disc where it's supposed to go, and thinks little of the phenomenon of gyroscopic precession. But the first helicopter pilots had to steer straight ahead if they wanted to turn left, and to the right, if they wanted to go straight ahead, and so on.

The first phenomenon of helicopter flight encountered was the tendency of the machine to want to spin in the opposite direction from the rotor. Anti-torque tail rotors or counterrotating main rotors solved this.

Pilots next learned to avoid maneuvers which turned the helicopter into a pendulum. These problems were encountered when helicopter flight was essentially hovering flight. As soon as attempts were made to see how fast over the ground the machine would move, they encountered a third problem, the *dissymmetry of lift*.

Both wings of a fixed aircraft are the same size, and this simply didn't occur with airplanes. The right and left wings moved through the air at the same speed, and the aerodynamic force applied to each wing was the same.

But the wings of a helicopter don't move through the air at the same speed. In a two-bladed helicopter, one blade, or wing, is advancing through the air while the other is retreating through the air. The speed of the advancing rotor blade tip is the speed at which it's turning (normally 600 feet per second) *plus* the speed of the helicopter through the air (at 100 knots, 170 feet per second). In this case, the sum would be 770 feet per second. The retreating blade, however, would be moving 600 feet per second *less* the 170 feet per second of the helicopter's movement through the air, or 430 feet per second.

And since lift depends on how fast the

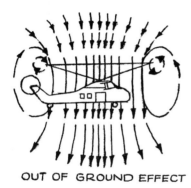

OUT OF GROUND EFFECT

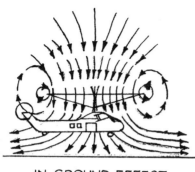

IN GROUND EFFECT

Wind flow in and out of ground effect.
(*Emma J. Butterworth*)

airfoil is moving through the air, this provided a lopsided lift. As the helicopter ap-
proached high speeds, the nose would tip
up sharply. On a counterclockwise rotor, the
greater lift was on the right, but the 90°
gyroscopic progression applied here as well:
the effect was a lifted nose.

It was necessary to incorporate a system
which would, as the blades moved around
and around, change the *angle of attack* of
the airfoil, so that the lift of both the advancing and retreating blades would be
equal. More *pitch* is added to the retreating
blade, and pitch is reduced on the advancing blade, in proportion to the speed of the
helicopter through the air.

One paper theory proved itself in flight.

A helicopter moving through the air, off the
ground, requires less power than a helicopter hovering.

A helicopter suspended in the air, but
not moving over the ground, represents
the pure theory of helicopter flight. At
some point, the rotary wings acquire enough
lift to raise the machine in the air. Lift has
overcome weight.

But at a hover, the air through which
the rotors move must be pulled in from
the surrounding atmosphere. The rotor becomes a giant fan as well as a wing, sucking
the air to it before using the air to suspend
itself. It amounts to turning the helicopter
into a machine that must swim upstream
in a rapids of its own making.

A helicopter hovering close enough to
the ground so that the air pulled through
its rotor disc is compressed, and seems to
form sort of a cushion for the helicopter,
in what is known as "the ground effect"
doesn't require as much power as a hovering helicopter out of ground effect. However,
hovering in ground effect generally blows
dust, small rocks, and other debris up
around the helicopter itself, where it's
sucked into the engine, greatly reducing
engine life.

The hover, within the ground effect, or
especially outside it, is the most unsatis-
factory facet of rotary wing flight. But it is
this same characteristic of being able to
hover motionless in the air that makes it
valuable to the Army.

The hover is one of the three attitudes
of helicopter flight. First a pilot applies
enough pitch to his rotor blades so that the
forces of lift overcome weight and drag, and
the helicopter becomes airborne. In a
normal takeoff, he then lowers the nose
of the machine, at the same time tilting
the forward edge of the rotor disc down-
ward. This causes forward motion over the
ground. As soon as the machine begins to
move at all, it begins to move into "new,"

or undisturbed air. This supply of "free" air reduces the amount of power required to obtain air from the surrounding atmosphere necessary in a hover.

At about 18 knots, the helicopter is moving fast enough so that all the air passing through the rotors is "free" air, and the air supply problem is eliminated. Since all the power is now applied to the generation of lift forces, the helicopter passing through *"translation lift"* now accelerates rapidly and rises quickly in the air.

At the instant translational lift becomes effective, the pilot must normally push his cyclic control forward to keep the nose from rising abruptly. Immediately after this, as forward flight increases the efficiency of the tail rotor, and at the same time streamlines the tailboom, another control movement is necessary. When these corrections have been made, and the helicopter is moving at more than eighteen knots or so, and out of ground effect, it is said to be in the third attitude, forward flight.

In forward flight, the helicopter is technically an air*plane,* a heavier-than-air machine passing through the air as a result of the aerodynamic force upon its airfoil. It is not a very effective airplane, compared to a fixed wing machine.

SIX

Coming of Age

Hanna Reitsch, the famous German woman pilot, flew the Focke-Angelis FA-61 helicopter as far back as 1937. With the help of Dr. Joseph Goebbels, this flight became world-famous. In truth, however, what Hanna Reitsch flew that day in Berlin's Sportspalast was little more than a laboratory experiment.

It was a significant contribution to aviation, laboratory experiment or not. The FA-61 *was* the first successful helicopter. It took off vertically, flew out of ground effect in forward flight and landed. It used two counterrotating rotors, suspended on booms to either side of its fuselage. It proved, said Dr. Goebbels, the brilliance of German aeronautical engineering. Colonel Charles A. Lindbergh, the hero, ventured to suggest that the Americans could well learn something from the Germans and was promptly vilified for this and other professional judgments about German aerial skill. If the Nazis had done it, reasoned our press, ergo, it was bad.

Lindbergh's friend, Igor I. Sikorsky, certainly no lover of the Nazis, was well aware of the Focke-Angelis machine, and regarded it as the honest accomplishment it was. But he wasn't especially impressed with the technique. Outrigger rotors, while they worked in this application, seemed to present overwhelming problems for the evolution of the machine. Sikorsky remained convinced, as he has to this day, that the most effective helicopter is one with one large rotor and one anti-torque tail rotor.

A thirteen-year-old boy in Berkeley, California, however, had the presumption to agree with the Focke-Angelis engineers that counterrotating rotors were the best solution to the problem of torque, and to disagree with Igor I. Sikorsky, at least so far as the Sikorsky main and countertorque rotor theories went.

Perhaps the most significant contribution to aviation that the Focke-Angelis helicopter actually made was to inspire thirteen-year-old Stanley Hiller, for Hiller was no ordinary adolescent.

At ten, Hiller had demonstrated his genius and terrified his neighbors by sending aloft over Berkeley a gunpowder-powered rocket plane, complete to swept-back wings.

Bowing to public and parental outrage, Hiller next turned his attention to conventionally powered model airplanes. Dissatisfied with the miniature gasoline engines available for youthful birdmen, he designed his own. Soon this bored him, and he began to use his miniature engine to power model racing cars. Dissatisfied with the model cars then being offered for sale, he designed and built his own. The Hiller racing cars were so good, and so soon in such demand that, at fifteen, he founded Hiller Industries, to make and market them nationally. The tolerant smiles for the youth's grandiose schemes soon faded. Within a year of its birth, Hiller Industries was grossing $100,-000 annually.

Hiller first proved the commercial value of his inventive genius by patenting a technique of aluminum die-casting, one of the reasons his miniature cars were the best on the market.

Having conquered that much of the world, Hiller was looking for another area where a hard-working, talented young man could make some money. In the newspaper, Hiller later recalled, he saw a photograph of Sikorsky's first (1939) VS-300. That reminded him of the pictures he had seen two years before, of the Focke-Angelis helicopter.

They were both right, and both wrong, Hiller decided. Counterrotating rotors were the answer, but not suspended on booms. The way to do this, Hiller thought, was to put counterrotating rotors on one shaft, one above the other.

He had money, and he recruited a staff, rented a hangar at the Oakland airport,

Stanley Hiller (third from right) and his original staff with the XH-44. (*Fairchild Hiller*)

Hiller demonstrates the stability of his helicoper by flying it "hands-off."

(Fairchild Hiller)

and proceeded to build the XH-44. X for Experimental, H for Hiller, and -44 for the year.

The first test flight was made from the driveway of Hiller's home in Berkeley. Like Igor Sikorsky, he reasoned that since it was his idea, it was only right that he be the test pilot. At the time, he had never seen a helicopter in flight, much less ridden in one, or received pilot training. At that time, no one west of the Mississippi River had ever seen a helicopter in flight.

The first flight was a qualified success: successful in that it got off the ground, and hovered uncertainly in what Hiller couldn't have known was the ground effect before tipping on its side and smashing its blades against the Hiller lawn.

Undiscouraged, Hiller rebuilt the XH-44. Three months later, with Hiller again at the controls, he flew it successfully from San Francisco's Marina Green.

The future looked bright. After another flight demonstration in the University of California stadium, nineteen-year old Hiller found himself a partner of Henry J. Kaiser. If Henry J. Kaiser saw merit in Hiller, the U. S. Navy reasoned, there was likely to be something in him worth some of the taxpayer's research money. Some was advanced, and more was promised, and the Hiller-copter Division of the Kaiser Cargo Corporation began to build its first and, as it turned out, only model, the X-2-235A.

At that point, the war ended. The Navy experienced the same cutback in appropriations the Army had undergone. No more Navy funds were advanced. Kaiser, too, lost some of his enthusiasm for the helicopter. Hiller announced that at least three million dollars in development money would be needed before Kaiser could begin to produce a helicopter for every garage.

Kaiser, on solemn reflection, and admitting that there was going to be a tremendous postwar market for transportation, decided that the best way to get his share of this market was in automobiles. He'd manufacture automobiles. He even had the names picked out. The *Frazer,* the *Kaiser,* and for the real mass market, the *Henry J.*

Hiller's problem, for the moment, was not the finer points of aerodynamics, but rather the cold print on his balance sheet. He had to find money.

In 1943, a group of aeronautical engineers, headed by a man named Frank Piasecki, decided they could build a helicopter as well as anyone else, and possibly a little better. They formed the P-V Engineering Forum and proceeded to build a helicopter, following Sikorsky's single main rotor ideas.

It flew and was successful, but Piasecki and others decided that the most effective system would be two equal-sized, counter-rotating rotors. Like Hiller, they had attracted the attention of the U. S. Navy. Unlike Hiller, they were skilled in dealing with the sometimes mysteriously motivated federal government.

Not only did they succeed in getting what is known as "development money," they actually succeeded in getting a contract to build a helicopter from scratch. In this regard, they beat Igor Sikorsky to the cash register. Sikorsky first built his, and only after it had flown sold it to the Army Air Forces.

The P-V Engineering Forum, Incorporated's XHRP-1, was considerably larger than Sikorsky's machine too, starting a bigger-and-faster rivalry between the two that goes on today. It had a standard, large transport aircraft engine, a 600-hp. Pratt & Whitney R-1340 engine powerful enough

Stanley Hiller and a disciple in a prototype of the H-23 (note windshield, rather than bubble) prove its inherent stability by leaving the cockpit high over San Francisco Bay.

(Fairchild Hiller)

The 10-passenger Piasecki XHRP-1, the prototype of the H-21. (*U. S. Army*)

to lift the ten-man machine through the air.

The Navy was delighted with the P-V Engineering Forum, Incorporated's XHRP-1, to the point where a contract for twenty of them was granted, despite postwar appropriations cutbacks. The machine was known as the Piasecki, and in 1946, the name of the company was changed to the Piasecki Helicopter Corporation. It was a going concern almost from the beginning.

That made three helicopter designers convinced of the future of rotary wing aircraft. The dean, Sikorsky; highly skilled Frank Piasecki, and the not-quite-old-enough-to-vote Stanley Hiller. A fourth aeronautical genius was on the scene, not missing a trick.

This was Larry Bell. He'd started in aviation as a mechanic, worked for the major airplane builders of the time, and in 1935, with little more than his confidence in the future of aviation and himself, he founded the Bell Aircraft Company.

Like Igor Sikorsky, Bell recognized that the helicopter was a great idea, but not quite yet. And like Sikorsky, Bell knew that money is the handmaiden of aviation development. He turned his attention to fixed wing aircraft.

And he made significant contributions: to aviation generally, to the defense of America, and to his bank balance. His friends in the Army Air Forces were aware the German aeronautical engineers were working on jet propulsion to replace the propeller. With war about to begin, it was no longer fashionable to pooh-pooh German accomplishments, but rather to study them (with the help of people like Lindbergh) and find out how to surpass them.

The Army Air Forces turned to Larry Bell to catch up. They gave him a blank check so far as research funds were concerned, and for war-scarce materials, and told him to build a jet airplane. In less than thirteen months, the Bell XP-59 flew at Murdoc Dry Lake, California.

It wasn't the only Bell accomplishment. The Bell P-39 Aircobra, with a cannon firing through its propeller hub was also the first fighter plane to have a tricycle landing gear. A twin-engine version of this, the Airacuda, was the first twin-engine escort fighter. What Bell, that staunch capitalist, thought when most of his planes were shipped to Communist Russia is not recorded.

Bell was also responsible for the first plane (the Bell X-5) to successfully alter the sweep of its wings while in flight; for the first radio-controlled bomb; and the first plane, the Bell X-1A, to fly at Mach 2.5, two-and-one-half times the speed of sound.

But he didn't lose sight of the helicopter. And there was enough money now to spend some on some solid research, development, and experimentation. A small garage in Buffalo, New York, was rented, and thirty people hired. Chief among them was Arthur Young, and there was also a talented young apprentice named Bartram Kelley.

Young brought with him to Bell a flying model helicopter. He had taken the approach that if he could come up with a technically feasible machine, the details of its construction could be worked out. The "engine" of Young's flying model had come from a discarded vacuum cleaner. The engine was light enough to be airborne, and its one-third horsepower was sufficient to make the model fly, even if it had to be plugged into a socket. From the beginning, Young used stabilizer bars on the rotor head, a design feature still in use, and relatively unchanged on today's helicopters.

What Young's flying model amounted to was more than the cheapest "test bed" helicopter ever devised. Watching the machine in flight over long periods was possible, even if it had to be plugged in and controlled from the ground. The model used a flywheel for stabilization, however, and this was obviously impractical for a full size, man-carrying helicopter.

Young devised a system which permitted control of cyclic pitch by use of a fixed stick control. This design feature too was

sound from the beginning and is still in use in the latest helicopters.

The first Bell helicopter, the Model 30, with Art Young at the controls, flew at Gardenville, New York, July 29, 1943. It was a one-man machine, with an open cockpit, a tricycle landing gear, and powered by a 165-horsepower Franklin engine capable of propelling the machine over the ground at 100 miles per hour. Bartram Kelley, now Bell's vice-president of engineering, recalls that at 20-knots, the first Model 30 tried very hard to shake itself apart.

Bell's present chief test pilot, Floyd Carlson, then a new employee of the new company, learned to fly the Model 30 on a tether, a steel cable, tying the machine to the ground. First he learned to make it move, and then to rise to the length of the cable. Finally, he was able to hover the machine in the air with slack in the cable.

Now visibly an expert, he and Young could now begin to teach others how to fly. The Model 30, through evolution, became the Model 47. The fabric covered, airplane type fuselage gave way to the pipe-frame work and Plexiglas bubble now so common to light helicopters. Finally, the wheels gave way to skids.

When the Army purchased its first Bell Model 47s in 1947, they were given the Army nomenclature, H-13. The Army purchase came after the sale of ten helicopters in 1946, the first helicopters ever certified by the government as safe enough for commercial use. Twenty years later, Bell Model 47s are in use all over the world. In late 1945, a semi-official agreement was reached between the Ground Forces and the Air Forces to have some Army pilots trained as helicopter pilots. The first army Aviator to be trained in this manner was Captain R. J. Ely. In early 1946, after perhaps a dozen Army pilots had learned, one way or another, the techniques of rotary wing

The maiden flight of the Bell Model 30 Helicopter. Art Young is the pilot. The date is July 29, 1943. (*Bell Aircraft*)

flight, the Army arranged for the purchase of a baker's dozen of Bell H-13s, and the contract provided, as the first contract for any military aircraft had, that the manufacturer teach the new owners how to fly their product.

Four artillery officers were sent to the Bell plant, then still in Buffalo, New York, to become helicopter pilots. Lieutenant Colonel Jack L. Marinelli, he of the skichute landing strip in Italy's Apennines during the war, was the ranking man. The others were Major Jack Blohm, and Captains Darwin P. Gerard and Hubert D. Gaddis.

By 1947, a formal agreement with the Air Forces provided for the Air Corps to conduct primary helicopter training for the Army at San Marcos, Texas. The first class, which began on September 1, 1947, was both something of a disappointment to the Army, and foreshadowed bitter, if polite, battles between the two services over aviation that would follow.

Instead of simply sending the Army pilots through the rather comprehensive standard Air Corps training program, then being conducted using Sikorsky R-5s, and R-6s, the Air Corps set up a separate school for Army pilots, using H-13s. The special Army course gave twenty-five hours of flight instruction. The Army felt this was inadequate and said so. The Air Corps reply, in effect, was that since the Air Corps didn't try to tell the Army how to teach people to shoot cannons, the Army would please not tell the Air Corps how to teach people how to fly.

The battle lines were drawn. Organic

Senator Harry S. Truman and Larry Bell with the Model 30, 1943. (*Bell Aircraft*)

The Bell H-13 (now OH-13). (*Author's Collection*)

Army aviation, so far as the Air Forces was concerned, was fine, just so long as it was limited to puddle-jumpers. When, however, it showed signs of competing for the taxpayers' dollars, it became a horse of an utterly different hue.

The Air Forces, throughout all of World War II, had been the *Army* Air Forces, under the authority of the Secretary of War. The Navy had its own Secretary, and the Air Forces figured this was what it wanted, too.

The Congress, for a long time, hadn't been wholly delighted with the organization of this country's means of waging war. There were justifiable howls of outrage over wasted taxpayers' money. The Navy would sell something as being surplus to its needs that the Army was buying at a high price. Each service had its own sacred ideas of what cut and color, for example, should be the underwear of its enlisted men.

The Congress, trying again to be all things to all people, decided *unification* of the Armed Forces was the solution to the problem. Unification would put soldiers, sailors, airmen, and Marines under one single head. To achieve unification, the Department of Defense was set up by the National Security Act of 1947. Under the Secretary of Defense would be three Secretaries. One for the Navy as before, charged with running the Navy and the Marine Corps. The office of the Secretary of War was abolished and replaced by that of the Secretary of the Army, charged with running the Army. And a whole new branch of service, the United States Air Force complete with its own Secretary, was established, to guide this nation's military activities in the air.

It wasn't quite so simple as it sounded. Areas where unification seemed not only sensible and practical but entirely possible, were blandly ignored by the brass. In one of their rare agreements Air Force generals agreed with the Navy admirals and Army generals that Navy broken legs, Air Force impacted teeth, and Army contagious diseases differed so much from broken limbs, painful teeth, and mumps in the other services that each service must maintain its own complete medical service.

All services were soon to share the provisions of the Universal Code of Military Justice, 1949, but this did not deter the Army, the Navy, and the Air Force from each setting up their own corps of legal officers with no interchange possible or permitted.

The top brass of the three services met at Key West, Florida, and attempted to clearly spell out just what each was expected to do in the defense of the United States. On April 21, 1948, over the signature of Secretary of Defense James V. Forrestal, a directive entitled "Functions of the Department of Defense and Its Major Components" was issued. It was a rather formal document, and each service promptly began to interpret what it said to its own liking.

The Air Force function was the shorter of the three:

"The Department of the Air Force is responsible for the preparation of the air forces necessary for the effective prosecution of war except as otherwise assigned, and, in accordance with integrated mobilization plans, for the expansion of the peacetime components of the Air Force to meet the needs of war.

"The Air Force, within the Department of the Air Force, includes aviation forces, both combat and service, not otherwise assigned."

Aside from the observation that the integration mentioned applied to Army-Navy-Air Force, and not of the races, the big loophole in this statement of functions are the three words applying to aviation forces "not otherwise assigned."

The Navy had a large air arm of its own, and the Marines, part of the Navy, had theirs too.

The functions of the Navy were spelled out as follows:

"The Department of the Navy is responsible for the preparation of Navy and Marine Corps forces necessary for the effective prosecution of war, except as otherwise assigned, and in accordance with integrated mobilization plans, for the expansion of the Navy and Marine Corps to meet the needs of war.

"Within the Department of the Navy, the Navy includes naval combat and service forces and such aviation as may be organic therein, and the Marine Corps includes not less than three combat divisions and three air wings, and such other land combat, aviation, and other services as may be organic therein."

The Navy, in other words, was permitted to retain its own aviation, plus three Marine divisions of foot soldiers, and Marine aviation. The Navy's army and air force was intact.

The Army's first statement of function was stated in the same words as the Air Force's and the Navy's, substituting "land forces" for "air forces" and "Navy and Marine forces."

The second function read as follows:

"The Army, within the Department of the Army, includes land combat and service forces, and such aviation and water transport as may be organic therein."

The Army, in other words, was forbidden to have battleships or heavy bombers; the Navy was forbidden to have *less* than three divisions of foot soldiers and the three wings of aviation considered necessary for their support; and the Air Force, by inference, wasn't supposed to either form an Armored Force or go into the submarine business.

Such was the bureaucratic gobbledy-gook

with which the roles and missions of the various services were pronounced. And no sooner was it printed than the legal eagles began both to search it carefully for loopholes and to make supplementary gentleman's agreements. The most significant of these, so far as Army aviation was concerned, was the weight agreement. It was a repeat of the Army Air Forces position of 1942, when it agreed to let artillery have aircraft, so long as they were "low performance aircraft of the Piper Cub type." The brand of aircraft wasn't spelled out this time, nor was the phrase "low performance" used. Instead, Army fixed wing aircraft were limited to a gross weight of 5000 pounds. The Air Force considered aircraft no heavier than 5000 pounds to be no threat to their reason for being. And, further, if the Army had aircraft of this size, it would relieve the Air Force of the nuisance of having them themselves.

The Key West Agreement spelled out the Air Forces' responsibility: "To furnish close combat and logistical air support to the Army, to include air lift, support, and resupply of airborne operations, aerial photography, tactical reconnaissance, and interdiction of enemy land power and communications."

On its face, that primary obligation of the Air Force seemed to solve all of the Army's problems. Air Force planes, went the theory, would not only first bomb and strafe a target before the Army arrived to take and hold it, either in Navy ships, or in Air Force aircraft, but further, Air Force planes would supply and resupply the engaged Army forces if necessary. Air Force planes would take aerial photographs for the Army's intelligence agencies, and Air Force planes would not only provide tactical reconnaissance of enemy ground forces but interdict, or strike, any of the enemy they detected.

The reality was something less than the perfection of the theory. In private conversation, the relationship between the Marines and the Navy Air Arm was pointed to as proof that their argument was more than intellectual bickering. The Navy, which owned the Marines, recognized that effective air support of ground operations was dependent upon immediate response to the needs of the ground commander. The only way to accomplish this, to strip away the red tape and cut reaction time to the absolute minimum, was to place the aircraft under the thumb of the ground commander.

Hence, said the Army, the recognized greater effectiveness of Marine Air Support over Air Force support of the Army. When a Marine division commander wanted air support, whether fighters, fighter bombers, or an emergency resupply mission by transport aircraft, he *ordered* it. It wasn't necessary for him to ask for it, through channels, to "justify" his request for some Air Force staff officer to approve or deny.

The Air Force said, nonsense. We know all about aircraft. We know how best to use them for the over-all good of the country. We are both relieving the ground commander of the necessity for deciding the most effective use of available aircraft and at once providing just that. The merits of the arguments weren't nearly as germane to the resolution of the disagreement as the Key West Agreement was. The Air Force simply referred to the Key West Agreement, where the roles and responsibilities of the Army and the Air Force were spelled out quite clearly. The Air Force had the right to run air power as they saw fit. The Army could like it or lump it.

There was nothing the Army could do but try to walk that narrow line between letter of the law and deceit. They turned, publicly, to doing the best they could with what was authorized to them.

SEVEN

Korea

As THE Air Force was anxious to get out from under the Army's control, there were many officers within the Army in the late 1940s who were anxious to have the Army relieved of the responsibility for aircraft, and who believed that the Army should have gotten rid of all its aircraft at the time of the reorganization of the defense establishment, in 1948.

Tactical commanders, past and present, however, exercises the greatest influence within the Army, and literally without exception, every tactical commander wanted light aircraft around, and under his control.

There were, for the Army, which wasn't supposed to fly very much at all, a rather astonishing number of airplanes. Some of them were left over from World War II, and some had been developed as a result of the experience of light Army Aviation during the war. There were, for example, 3972

A Stinson L-5 at Fort Riley, Kansas. (*Collection Col. L. Ballantine*)

The Air Forces' Interstate L-6.
(*U. S. Air Force*)

The Army Air Forces leased, in 1942, one of
these Ryan airplanes and named it the L-10.
(*U. S. Air Force*)

The L-13. (*Author's Collection*)

L-5s, purchased for Army use between 1942, the year of greatest procurement (1731 airplanes), and 1945, when 115 were bought. This was the same sort of civilian light airplane as the Pipers and the Taylorcrafts and the Aeroncas, drafted into the Army, and like the men who flew it, still showing the colors of a civilian through the hastily applied olive drab paint. The Vultee-Stinson L-5, called the Sentinel was more powerful than the Grasshoppers, with a 185-hp engine.

The Air Forces in 1942–43 bought 251 L-6s for their liaison squadrons. This was another puddle-jumper, manufactured by a company called Interstate and powered by a 102-hp Franklin engine. A modification of the L-7, the L-8A, came off the drawing boards, but only eight planes actually left the assembly lines, and these were all given to Bolivia.

The L-7A was another puddle-jumper, a 90-hp Franklin engine-driven two-seater. There were nineteen in all of these, and all of them were sent to France in 1944.

Twenty Stinson Voyagers, three-passenger, 90-hp puddle-jumpers, were called into service, painted olive drab, designated the L-9, and given to the British Navy under Lend-Lease.

There was just one L-10, the name given by the services to the Ryan SCW, and it never really was sworn in for active duty. The three-passenger, 145-hp craft was leased by the government during 1942. There was one L-11, a six-passenger, 600-hp Bellanca 31–50. It also served as a leased ship in Army colors during 1942.

There were four L-12s, four passenger Stinsons. Two of them had 300-hp Pratt & Whitney engines, and two 300-hp Lycomings. They were used as trainers by the Army Air Corps in 1944.

The L-13, a 245-hp three-passenger plane was tested by the Army Ground Forces in 1945, and found somehow wanting; they were not accepted. However, there was a change of mind somewhere in the procurement agencies, for as late as June of 1951, there were 43 L-13s on the Army's books.

Piper made another bid for Army aircraft business with the L-14 in 1945. This carried pilot, observer, and two passengers. It had a 130-hp Lycoming engine. Army Ground bought a total five of them in 1945 –46.

The L-15, built by Boeing, tried to be all things to all services. It supposedly incorporated all the good characteristics of a liaison and observation aircraft, and at the same time was supposed to have done away with most of the annoying features. The Army bought ten of them in 1949. Very quietly, without procuring any more, the Army discreetly transferred the 125-hp two place aircraft to the Alaskan Foresty Service.

The L-16, an improved Aeronca, fared somewhat better. The two-place machine was first bought in 1947. In June 1948, there were sixty-one 85-hp L-16As on the Army's books, and a year later, 742 L-16Bs, the same ship with a 90-hp engine. Most of these were given to the Civil Air Patrol between 1952 and 1954.

The L-17 was the North American Aviation Company's Navion, a low-wing, four-place machine powered by Continental engines developing as much as 205-hp. The first was purchased in 1947, and, at one time or another, they were fairly common in the Army, generally assigned to a division or corps headquarters, primarily as a small personnel transport. On June 30, 1951, there were forty-two L-17As on the Army's books; on January 1, 1950, there were 196 L-17Bs, and there was a total of thirty-five of the final model, the L-17C on June 30, 1949. The L-17 saw much service in Korea.

The L-18 was another two-passenger Piper, still a puddle-jumper with a 90-hp engine. The Army bought 1043 of them al-

The L-15. (*U. S. Army*)

The Aeronca L-16.
    (*Collection Col. L. Ballantine*)

The North-American L-17, the "Navion." (*U. S. Army*)

An early Cessna L-19. (*Collection Col. L. Ballantine*)

An early De Havilland of Canada L-20 "Beaver." (*De Havilland*)

The Piper L-21. (*U. S. Air Force*)

together, starting in 1949. Most of them were sent to Turkey as military assistance. L-18s assigned to the Turkish Army showed up in Korea with the Turkish Battalion while the Army was still flying L-4s, and L-16s and L-17s, and before the L-19 got there.

The first L-19s (now O-1s) were delivered to the Army late in 1950, and this aircraft is still in use by the Army. It's a two-place, high-wing Cessna powered by a 213-hp Continental engine. Before the Vietnamese War made production and in-use figures of value to the enemy and classified, the Army reported that it had more than two thousand of them in use. There has been additional procurement, and many have been furnished to American allies the world over. The Air Force bought some of these Army-developed aircraft for the use of its forward air controllers, and for other missions of the Tactical Air Command and the Air Commandos.

The L-20 (now U-6), a six place, ton-carrying high-winged utility transport was designed by De Havilland of Canada for use as a bush plane in the Canadian and Alaskan wilds. When the Korean War broke, the Army bought it, off the shelf, painted it olive drab, and sent it to Korea, where it quickly earned a reputation for being a very practical airplane, and the most forgiving. It has a 450-hp Pratt & Whitney engine. Again, before strength and procurement figures became classified, the Army admitted having more than 650 of these, and more have certainly been procured.

The L-21 was a Piper again, the Super Cub. There were two models, L-21A and L-21B, both powered by 135-hp Lycoming engines. There were at one time 150 L-21As, mostly used to train pilots for the Korean War, and sixty-nine L-21Bs, most of which were sent to the Far East until L-19 production met Korean War demands. Both models of the L-21 have been dropped by the Army.

The L-22 was a Super Navion, an improved L-17, with a 260-hp engine. The Army bought four of these.

As a result of a great shortage of light aircraft in the opening days of the Korean War, the Army had to buy whatever light aircraft came close to meeting its requirements. One of these, another ship developed for use in the Arctic bush country, was the LC-126, a 300-hp Cessna. There were about seventy in all, most of them used in Alaska, and then sent to Fort Rucker, Alabama, for use as instrument flight training ships.

During the Korean War, bringing this phase to Army Aviation to sort of a milestone, the Army acquired its first twin-engined machine, bought off the shelf from the Beech Aircraft Corporation, which called it the Twin Bonanza. The first of these was sent to Korea, where, as the L-23 (now U-8), it was used to ferry the highest brass (Ridgway, Van Fleet, Taylor, I. D. White, and others) around that rocky country.

The Korean War established in the mind of the Army, beyond any doubt whatever, that aviation, fixed and rotary wing, and under Army control was an absolute necessity.

Despite the number of aircraft in the inventory, it became immediately apparent, from the first day of that war, that available stocks, and even projected procurement, were not going to be anywhere near adequate for what had to be done.

There were a handful of American troops in Korea when that war began, and they were under the direct orders of the Department of the Army, in Washington, rather than under General of the Army Douglas MacArthur's headquarters across the Sea of Japan, in Tokyo. What troops, including what few aircraft there were, were engaged in training a South Korean Army, and were organizationally, as well as numerically, unable to form any sort of a force to resist the North Koreans.

The Cessna LC-126. (*Collection Col. L. Ballantine*)

This L-23-A, Number A21801, was the first twin-engine airplane in the Army.

(*Beech Aircraft*)

Major General Edward M. Almond, Commander of the Inchon Invasion and Chief of Staff to MacArthur. (*U. S. Army*)

The word that the North Koreans had crossed the border came first to Major General (later Lieutenant General) Edward M. Almond, MacArthur's Chief of Staff, on Sunday, June 25, 1950. Almond had dropped by his office en route to the golf course, and was at his desk when the messages came in:

OPERATIONAL IMMEDIATE
SEOUL 0925 25 JUNE 1950
FROM MILITARY ATTACHE US EMBASSY
  SEOUL KOREA
FOR ASST CHIEF OF STAFF, INTELLIGENCE
DEPARTMENT OF THE ARMY WASHINGTON
  DC
INFO COPY TO G-2 HQ FAR EAST COMMAND
  TOKYO
AT 0400 HOURS THIS MORNING NORTH KOREAN FORCES AFTER AN ARTILLERY BARRAGE INVADED SOUTH KOREA. SEQUENCE OF ATTACK IS APPARENTLY WESTWARD FROM ONGJIN PENINSULA. MORE FOLLOWS.

OPERATIONAL IMMEDIATE
FOR COMMANDING GENERAL US AIR FORCE FAR EAST TOKYO FROM COMMANDER, US AIR FORCE, KIMPO AIR FORCE BASE SEOUL KOREA
THERE IS FIGHTING IN VICINITY 38TH PARALLEL. BELIEVE THIS IS MORE THAN BORDER VIOLATION. INVESTIGATING. MORE FOLLOWS.

By the time Almond notified General of the Army Douglas MacArthur, and Lieutenant General Walton H. Walker, the Eighth Army Commander, Army Aviation had already entered the fight. Two aviators of the Korean Military Advisory Group (KMAG), Major Lloyd Swink and Lieutenant Frank Brown, had voluntarily flown their L-5s to the Ongjin Peninsula to rescue the American advisers to the 17th Republic of Korea Infantry Regiment, already crumbling before the North Korean assault.

Soon Army airplanes were in the middle of the fight. Gasoline tanks were stripped from jeeps and installed in the back seats of L-5s to give them the necessary range to fly over the Sea of Japan.

On July 1, two L-17s were dispatched to Brigadier General John H. Church, whom MacArthur had ordered to Korea to assume command of advance American elements. On July 3, the first L-5s from MacArthur's forces in Japan were flown to Korea in formation with an L-17, the only Army aircraft with a radio which could use Air Force communications and navigation systems. On July 4, nine Army aviators of the 24th Division flew from their Japanese base to Taejon, Korea. That afternoon, at four o'clock, the first aerial artillery direction of the Korean War was accomplished by Lieutenant James E. Alvator.

From the beginning, Army Aviation played an important role in the Korean War. If it had not been possible to evacuate President Syngman Rhee from Seoul in the back seat of an Army L-5, he very likely would have fallen into the hands of the Communists, who had broadcast their intention to stand him against the wall.

Operation Dragonfly, the direction of fast Air Force fighters against targets on the ground by pilots of the low and slow L-5s, began on July 6 and lasted throughout the war, even after the Air Force eventually put target locating smoke rockets on primary trainers and tried to assume this function itself.

Army aircraft played a major role in the withdrawal of American and Korean forces to the Pusan perimeter, not only by directing air and artillery strikes, but by finding safe routes for the fleeing forces, locating lost units, and providing harried commanders with up to the minute location of the enemy.

Casualties came to aviation almost immediately. On July 7, 1950, Lieutenant Arvid O. Munson of the 24th Division was shot down near Taejon while directing artillery fire. His body was not recovered until after the Inchon invasion in September.

The function of Army Aviation in the opening days of the Korean War was about what it was in World War II. In World War II, generally speaking, there had been a plethora of supplies, but the reverse was true here. There was a shortage of planes. A shortage of parts. Because there had been small appropriations to keep pilots on flight pay, there was also a shortage of pilots, certainly the most important item on a military shopping list for Army Aviation.

When Lieutenant Alvator, for example, who had flown the first artillery direction mission, crawled battered and exhausted from his L-5, his mechanic, a corporal by the name of Cooler, crawled in. Not to taxi the plane to its parking place, but to take it aloft himself to do his share of artillery direction. For the moment, the Army looked the other way and ignored the sacred belief that only duly commissioned officers and gentlemen could fly.

Pilots in Army units as far away as Germany were hastily bundled into planes and sent to the Far East. From the Pentagon, telegrams were sent to men all over the country who had been solemnly assured that they would be called back into service only in the event of an all-out war. They were given two weeks to settle their affairs and report in uniform, promises not withstanding. Army aviation needed pilots, and right then. They answered the call, and they performed splendidly, even if they had rather bitter things to say about the personnel policies of the United States Army.

With economy no longer a consideration, a contract was let before the month of June 1950 was out for 420 Cessna L-19s. By December 1953, there were nearly two thousand of them in the Army.

Foot by bloody foot, yard by bloody yard, the United States Eighth Army retreated to the Pusan perimeter, while the L-5s and the L-17s of Army Aviation buzzed overhead.

And then on September 15, 1950, off the coast of Inchon, an invasion fleet appeared. The time and the place of the invasion has been considered utterly impractical by the Pentagon, but Douglas MacArthur, the acknowledged amphibious expert prevailed. The United States X Corps, some of whose units joined up literally at sea, Major General Edward M. Almond, commanding, successfully landed across the Inchon mud flats and cut the enemy's supply lines in half.

The supply economy of a peacetime Army affected all echelons, including the highest. There was a plane, a common, well-battered L-5, assigned to General Almond, the commander of the largest invasion force

Major General Clovis Byers, left, and the L-5 *Blue Goose* he inherited from General Almond on August 30, 1951. Center is one of her pilots, Lieutenant Robert A. Michelson and right is X Corps Air Officer, Lieutenant Colonel Joseph O'Hanlon. (*Signal Corps*)

ever formed in the Pacific, but there was no olive drab paint to protect it against the corrosion of the sea. It was painted blue, and promptly dubbed by Almond the *Blue Goose*. If no double entendre was intended, one was certainly implied by Almond's juniors.

The Army had no helicopter to provide the X Corps Commander. The man who was simultaneously Chief of Staff, Headquarters, Far East Command, Chief of Staff United Nations Command, and Commanding General, United States X Corps borrowed one from the First Marine Division which was under his command.

The invasion took place on the 15th of September. The next day, Captain Charles Keleman took his L-5 off from the deck of the aircraft carrier *Badoeng Straits* and headed for Kimpo Air Base north of Seoul. He didn't land, however, because the people he saw as he made his final approach were wearing the uniform of the North Korean Army. He returned to the aircraft carrier.

Two weeks from the moment of the first landing, Douglas MacArthur turned over to Syngman Rhee his recaptured capital city.

Before June 26, 1950, the Army had been given $2,000,000 to purchase aircraft during the 1951 fiscal year. The new budget called for $42,376,230, more than twenty-one times as much.

At the Aviation Section of the Artillery School at Fort Sill, a thirty-day refresher course for the recalled reservist pilots, 210 in all, was set up.

By March 1952 this reserve force was exhausted. Pilots had to be trained from scratch. Before the end of the war, almost 1500 pilots had graduated from flight school.

With Army aircraft overhead, the Eighth Army, under General Walker, broke out of its Pusan enclave and started North. Near Suwon, on the South Korean coast, the Eighth Army's 1st Cavalry Division joined up with units of the X Corps' 7th Infantry Division on September 26, 1950.

Shortly afterward, Eighth Army assumed responsibility for the Seoul Area, and the X Corps reboarded its ships, sailed around the Korean peninsula, and landed on the east coast of Korea at Wonsan.

On October 1, the Far East Command had officially announced that all resistance south of the 38th parallel had ended. On October 10, the ROK I Corps captured Wonson in time for the X Corps to land unopposed in North Korea. On October 26, ROK units reached the Yalu River.

But soon Army aviators began to report unpleasant news, that of a massive Chinese buildup across the Yalu. General Almond passed these reports onto MacArthur's Intelligence Chief, Major General Charles A. Willoughby, who didn't seem convinced.

A Corps Commander cannot, according to military custom, go directly to the overall commander. But Major General Almond was not only the X Corps Commanding General. He was still the Chief of Staff, Headquarters Far East Command, and Headquarters, United Nations Command. He took off, so to speak, his X Corps Commander's hat, and put on his Chief of Staff's hat. As Chief of Staff, he was over the G-2. And as Chief of Staff, he sent proof positive that the Chinese were about to enter the war. He sent an Air Force C-54 full of Chinese prisoners to Tokyo.

Almond's aerial surveillance in the *Blue Goose* of North Korea told him two things. First, that he couldn't hold his extended positions in the mountains against the overwhelming Chinese forces, and against the forces of nature. But, second, he knew he could hold Hamhung and Hungnam just as long as he wanted to. He so informed MacArthur, and began to make plans to withdraw to the coast.

The Chinese and winter struck the American Forces in North Korea at just about the same time. On November 20, the 7th Division had reached the Yalu. Less than a week later, on November 26, the Chinese struck in subzero weather.

For its operations during the last week in November 1950, which included the evacuation of more than eight hundred critically wounded men in light aircraft pressed into emergency medical service, the Air Section of the 7th Division was awarded the Distinguished Unit Citation, the first ever given an Army Aviation unit.

In a battle that took its place in history beside Gettysburg and Tarawa, elements of the 7th Division fought its way out of the mountains with the First Marine Division and to the relative safety of the Hamhung enclave.

The battleship *Missouri* appeared off Hamhung, the fire of its 18-inch cannon directed by Army pilots in Army aircraft.

On the western front, the Eighth Army was in deeper trouble. Their lines cracked under the Chinese assault and the second withdrawal began. The word used by the participants was bug-out. There was confusion, panic, even cowardice.

Almost unnoticed, at Ascom City, near Seoul, Captain Marcus L. Sullivan of Big Sandy, Texas, pulled up on his cyclic control and flew the first Army helicopter, a

Bell H-13B, into combat. Things were so confused that no one remembers the exact date. It was simply "after the Chinks came in."

In the Eighth Army area, as Christmas drew near, Army pilots equipped with extra maps flew over the mountains in search of lost and retreating American units. When they found one, a map marked to show the best path of withdrawal was dropped.

In the X Corps area, General Almond flew over his forces in the *Blue Goose,* picking in his mind the line behind which the X Corps would not retreat. But that wasn't to happen, either. Without the troops of the X Corps, the Eighth Army could not successfully resist the Chinese. Reluctantly, MacArthur ordered the evacuation of the X Corps from North Korea.

It was not a Dunkirk. General Almond, retired now and living in Anniston, Alabama, makes the point that the X Corps was ordered from Hamhung, not forced to leave by the enemy and that when it made its withdrawal, the X Corps took with it its equipment, more than 16,000 vehicles, all their artillery, their ammunition, their wounded, many of their dead and most important, their pride. They embarked at Hamhung a tactical unit and they disembarked at Pusan ready to fight.

The X Corps never bugged out. And Almond, its commander, received perhaps the finest compliment ever paid a soldier by a Marine. General Lewis B. "Chesty" Puller, the toughest Marine in the history of the Corps, called him "the finest combat commander I have ever known."

As the Chinese pushed the Eighth Army back to Seoul and then out of the South Korean capital, Captain Albert C. Sebourn of Fort Smith, Arkansas, flew the first Army helicopter "Med Evac" mission in Korea, picking a wounded soldier from the battlefield and flying him to a Mobile Army Surgical Hospital (MASH).

There were four pilots in Sebourn's brand-new unit, the Army's 2nd Helicopter Detachment. Two weeks after they entered the war, all four had been awarded the Distinguished Flying Cross for valor above and beyond the call of duty. Between January 1, and February 1, 1951, the 2nd Helicopter Detachment evacuated more than five hundred seriously wounded soldiers, many of them—in one instance twenty-three at one location—from units entirely surrounded by the enemy. Since the Chinese didn't respect the Red Cross and considered helicopters, no matter what their mission, fair game, the choppers carried no Red Cross insignia of the non-combatant. They flew ammunition and rations into besieged units and then flew the seriously wounded out.

The first helicopter evacuation of wounded, despite the Army's claims, did not take place in Korea, but during World War II, when Colonel Philip Cochran (the man made famous in the funnies by Milton Caniff as Colonel Flip Corcoran) of the 1st Air Commando Group used a one-passenger Sikorsky R-4 to evacuate wounded from behind-the-lines columns in Burma. The Air Force lists the date at May 3, 1943.

And in Korea, too, the Air Force is entitled to the credit for the first helicopter evacuation of wounded. Detachment F of the 3rd Air Rescue Unit began answering calls from Army commanders for the evacuation of wounded in early July 1950.

As a matter of fact, it was as a result of a joint and successful Army-Air Force experiment on August 3, 1950, at the Taegu Teacher's College that the Army's Surgeon General demanded that the Army provide suitably equipped helicopters for medical evacuation. The same experiment caused the Navy, in response to a demand from its medical officers, to install helicopter landing pads on Naval hospital ships.

With good reason, the military services generally give their medical personnel what-

May 12, 1951. Lieutenant General James A. Van Fleet prepares to inspect the 2nd Infantry Division sector from an H-13. (*U. S. Army*)

ever the medics think they want. Every soldier, Marine, and airman is wholly convinced that if he should be hit, everything possible will be done for him. The effect of this belief on morale is obvious.

As the Eighth Army, now reinforced by the X Corps, began first to slow the Chinese advance and then to stop it and then to counterattack, army Aviation played an important role. In February 1951, for example, the aviation section of the 2nd Infantry Division was credited with five thousand enemy casualties during the battle for Wonju.

In the spring, the first of the L-19s, the two-place, high-wing, 213-hp Cessna, ar-

rived in time to participate in the second recapture of Seoul. The first L-19 in the Army, number 01327 (which was used as a test and training aircraft and not sent to Korea) is in the Army Aviation Museum at Fort Rucker.

With the exception, however, of helicopter evacuation of the wounded, Army Aviation generally played about the same role in the Korean War as it had in World War II. There were more airplanes and they were gathered together in Light Aviation Sections rather than being assigned only to artillery units, but they performed basically the same roles of artillery spotting, visual reconnaissance and personnel transportation. The first Light Aviation Section was the 5th LAS of X Corps.

A wounded soldier is carried from an L-20 Beaver used as a flying ambulance.
(*De Havilland Aircraft*)

The interior of an L-20 used as an ambulance. To get the litter inside, it was necessary to cut a hole in the instrument panel. Photo taken November 27, 1952, at Kinsal, Korea.
(*U. S. Army*)

Tail Number 21803-The YL-23, prototype of the L-23s. Photo taken in March 1952.
(*Beech Aircraft*)

An H-19 of the 6th Aviation Company with a load of repatriated American prisoners, Panmunjom, April 20, 1953. (*U. S. Army*)

Captain Albert C. Sebourn (left) and SFC Hubert L. Tompkins demonstrate Sebourn's hastily designed and fabricated aerial litter basket for the H-13. This Korean photo is dated December 31, 1950. (*U. S. Army*)

A Sikorsky R-4 (foreground) of the type used by Colonel Philip Cochran, USAAC, to make the first helicopter evacuation of wounded. Rear is the twin-engine Sikorsky H-37.

(*Sikorsky Aircraft*)

Toward the end of 1952, the first of the Beavers arrived in Korea. These airplanes, the L-20, designed by De Havilland of Canada for use in the Canadian and Alaskan bush country, were bought off the shelf, painted olive drab and sent to the mountains of Korea, where they immediately proved their worth.

A Beechcraft Twin-Bonanza arrived in Korea under much the same conditions, fresh from the factory and wearing a new coat of olive-drab paint. As the L-23, it was flown by Captains James Leffler and Jay D. Leonard all over the peninsula, with passengers ranging from the Eighth Army Commander, Syngman Rhee and his Austrian wife to touring movie stars. A second L-23 arrived shortly before the war ended. Like the first L-19, the first prototype L-23 now rests at the Army Aviation Museum at Fort Rucker.

And just before peace came, a company of Sikorsky H-19 (now UH-19) helicopters arrived in Korea, but there was little time left in the fighting to do much more than experiment with them.

Once Army helicopters and pilots arrived in Korea, their hard work and devotion earned them the profound respect of their comrades-in-arms. Lieutenant Joseph Bowler, for instance, of the original 2nd Helicopter Detachment, flew 482 missions, during which he evacuated to the comforts of a hospital 824 seriously wounded soldiers. Lieutenant William P. Brake topped this record in 1952 by flying 545 missions and evacuating 900 wounded men.

By January of 1951, the 3rd and 4th Helicopter Detachments had arrived in Korea. Within a year of the first arrival, 5040 soldiers had been evacuated by helicopter; by the time the war ended, on July 27, 1953, the total was 21,212.

The pilots of these helicopters were not medical personnel, but rather artillery, armored and infantry officers, who happened to be pilots and available for the assignment. During 1952, the Medical Corps requested and received, permission to train its own pilots, officers of the Medical Service Corps, who, while not physicians, would be trained in medical technology as well as flight. The first Medical Service Corps pilots arrived in Korea a month after the armistice.

EIGHT

The Aviation Center

On the first day of the Korean Armistice, Lieutenant General Isaac Davis White, commander of the Army-sized X Corps Group (it contained, at its peak strength, three Korean Corps, plus all the troops of a reinforced U. S. Corps) was named Commander of the U. S. Fourth Army at Fort Sam Houston, Texas.

A formal change-of-command ceremony was held at his Kwandae-Ri, North Korea, command post. It was a stirring tribute to a distinguished soldier (the 17-gun salute was fired by tank cannon under the command of Captain George S. Patton III; when he actually left, two combat-grimy enlisted men held up a sign so crudely lettered that it had to be spontaneous reading FAREWELL, I D, WE'LL MISS YOU!) and something prophetic besides.

The brass of Eighth Army, of I Corps and IX Corps, of the Korean Army, and the Turks and the Greeks and the English and the rest of the UN forces were on hand. But they arrived not in shiny staff cars, or even well-polished jeeps, but by L-19 and helicopter.

They had left their headquarters all over the Korean peninsula just after lunch, and they would be back at their own headquarters in time for supper. In World War II, that sort of puddle-jumping was unique; by the end of the Korean War, rapid travel by senior officers in light aircraft had become as much a part of the army as stripes on a sergeant's sleeves.

It had gone even further than that. White's 5th Light Aviation Section (LAS), the first organic aviation unit in the Army, had for many months before the armistice scheduled liaison service, unofficially and universally called Teeny-Weeny Airlines. Using L-20 Beavers and L-17 Navions, L-19s and whatever helicopters were available, regularly scheduled service between the subordinate units of X Corps had carried pfcs and majors, newspapers and blood, jeep parts and ammunition, anything that could be carried in anything that would fly.

It was twelve minutes by chopper or L-17 from X Corps to the 45th Division, and an hour and a half by road. It was an hour to Eighth Army by air, and all day by road.

White had formed the 5th LAS by gathering together substantially all of the light aircraft (and their pilots) assigned to his subordinate units, leaving only those absolutely essential to the unit's mission (medical evacuation helicopters, for example, and artillery spotting L-19s) under the unit's direct control. The assembled aircraft were dispatched according to a system of priorities, and it was generally agreed that this was a far more efficient utilization of available aircraft and personnel.

There were advantages, too, in maintenance procedures, and in utilization of mechanics.

The commanders of the units which had lost their aircraft, however, were unhappy at the loss, although they were able to draw on the pooled aircraft for their needs. It was less a case of personal selfishness, a reluctance to give up something, than a manifestation of the rule that the more aircraft a commander had, the more roles he could find for them.

The Army tries hard, if it doesn't too often succeed, to learn from its experiences in wartime. Tables of Organization and Equipment (TO&E) are constantly under study, and after a war, generally undergo a complete overhaul.

There was no commander asked to comment on manning tables who felt that he didn't need as many aircraft as the TO&E provided. Without exception, the recommendations for changes included long, and almost irrefutable justifications for more aircraft of all types, with greater weight-carrying ability.

It wasn't a question of subtly suggesting that White had erred in forming a pool of aircraft, and that they really should have been left in their parent organizations. The concept of having a pool of aircraft on which all subordinate units could rely had proven sound. What the division commanders suggested was that there should be pools at all echelons of command, plus many more organic aircraft to accomplish the missions of specific units.

General Isaac Davis White, as a major general, shortly after he was ordered to halt his 2nd Armored "Hell on Wheels" Division in place and to let the Russians take Berlin. He was to retire with four stars, and as Commander in Chief, U. S. Army Pacific. (*U. S. Army*)

In the early days of the Korean War, a procurement contract had been given to the Sikorsky Helicopter Company for the H-19, a ten-passenger single-rotor transport helicopter.

The first H-19A was delivered in June of 1952. It had a 550-hp Pratt & Whitney R-1340-57 engine. By June of 1953, there were seventy-two H-19Cs in the Army inventory. They had undergone some testing by the Aviation Section of Army Field Forces Board Number One at Fort Sill as an aircraft, and elsewhere as equipment for a unit. Shortly before the armistice, the 6th

Transportation company (Helicopter) company equipped with the H-19 arrived in Korea.

Tests were conducted. The H-19 company proved able, for example, to air-lift an infantry company a distance of twenty-five miles with such facility and speed that no further question remained in the minds of any military planner about the value of the helicopter in Army operations. Before the newness had been worn off the H-19, Army planners wanted its successor, the eighteen-passenger, 1425 hp H-34 (now CH-34).

Military development and procurement can perhaps be described by simile: It is a huge ball, too often at rest, and resisting, according to the laws of physics, any attempt to get it moving. Once moving, however, it is difficult to stop, and hard to di-rect as it rolls down the hill, gathering speed and literally crushing anything in its path.

Army Aircraft Procurement had just a barely perceptible momentum when the Korean War began. As the annual appropriation for Army aircraft jumped from $2,000,000 to more than $42,000,000 for fiscal 1951, it began to roll with increasing speed. There were, for example, sixty-three Bell H-13 two-place observation or medical evacuation helicopters in the Army inventory when the Korean War began. By December 1954, six months after the Korean War, there were more than seven hundred H-13s, in various models. The Hiller H-23 (now OH-23), with just about the same characteristics, entered the Army inventory with the purchase of one helicopter during fiscal 1950. By December 1952, there were eighty-two H-23As, and there were almost two

Forecast of things to come: On February 24, 1953, Colonel Richard D. Meyers (extreme left) and Brigadier General Frank S. Besson (center, front) inspected a newly arrived H-19 at Ascom City, Korea. Meyers was to become a pilot and a lieutenant general before his retirement. Besson was to wear four stars and become commander of the U. S. Army Matériel Command. (U. S. Army)

The Sikorsky H-34. (*Sikorsky Aircraft*)

Bell H-13s of the Fourth Army precision-flying Square Dance Team. (*U. S. Army*)

A Korean War vintage Hiller H-23.
(*Defense Department*)

The Piasecki H-25 "Army Mule."
(*U. S. Army*)

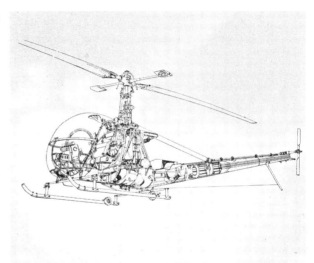

Cutaway drawing of the H-23.
(*Fairchild Hiller*)

An H-21 giving a lift to an H-13 in Korea,
1955. (*U. S. Army*)

The parking ramp at Fort Sill, Oklahoma, in May 1951. (*Collection Col. Archie Summers*)

hundred H-23Bs by the time of the armistice.

In 1953, the Army got its first H-25A (Army Mule), a six-passenger twin-rotor helicopter built by Piasecki. There were sixty-three of these by June 1955, a year after the Korean War. The first Piasecki H-21 (now CH-21), a large (twenty passenger, 1425-hp tandem rotor) transport helicopter joined the Army in August 1954, a month after the armistice. By January 1962, there were more than three hundred of them.

The helicopters and the fixed-wing aircraft added to the inventory were not, of course, suddenly introduced. They sort of trickled into the Army, one or two or a dozen machines a month, each requiring, in addition to pilots, mechanics, radio navigation equipment technicians, ground handlers, and the rest of the logistical support system.

The Army Aviation school had been located at Fort Sill, Oklahoma, as part of the Artillery School since the beginning of organic Army Aviation. Army Aviation had begun as an aerial observation platform for the direction of field artillery, and training aviators for that purpose had been a logical function of the Artillery School.

After Korea, Army Aviation was no longer regarded by anyone as a pure, or even substantial, function of artillery. Furthermore, interbranch rivalry had raised its head. The other combat arms were not happy at the prospect of having artillery dominate what was obviously going to be a major function of the Army as a whole.

It was decided that an Army Aviation school, separate from the Artillery School, was the logical answer. There were a number of political considerations involved in the closing of the Aviation School at Fort Sill, and the simultaneous opening of the Aviation School at Fort Rucker, Alabama, in August 1954, a month after the armistice.

It had become apparent by then that the Army was to have helicopter transport companies. Under the Key West Agreement, or of modifications to it, the Air Force was supposed to train helicopter pilots for the Army.

It was the Army's studied judgment that the vast bulk of helicopter pilots should be warrant officers. A warrant officer, the Army reasoned, was almost by definition a highly skilled specialist, who, although given officer privileges, and pay raising as high as that given a major, would spend his military career in his speciality. He would not be trained in higher level Army schools, nor given command of a unit, or anything of the kind. He would be, for his period of service, a specialist.

It was the Army's studied judgment, further, that the way to establish such a corps of professional helicopter pilots was to solicit enlisted men to go to flight school. On graduation, they would become both pilots and warrant officers. The Army would handle the training of the enlisted men, to teach them how to conduct themselves as officers, and the Air Force, according to the Key West Agreement, would teach them to fly.

The Air Force announced that it was perfectly willing to teach anyone the Army sent them to fly helicopters, providing only that (a) he first be a qualified fixed-wing pilot and (b) already be either an officer or a warrant officer. It was the Air Force's studied judgment that an Army pilot-training program, closely following their World War II Aviation Cadet program, would be a failure, and, further that their experience had shown them that being able to fly a fixed-winged airplane was an absolute prerequisite for rotary-wing pilot training.

In the last full summer of the Korean War, 1953, the Army received permission to conduct its own flight training. The Air Force, believing the Army's project was destined for failure, gave them the rope with which they would hang themselves. Once the program proved a success, however, there was little the Air Force could do to resume its control of Army helicopter flight training.

The success of the Aviation Warrant Officer Candidate program, however, posed other problems for the Army. The influx of helicopters required that more and more pilots be trained. There was a concurrent, but smaller, demand for fixed-wing pilots. A school, a private school, so to speak, was needed.

A board of officers was selected to pick a suitable site for the new school, once Department of Defense permission had been granted. A number of sites were proposed, including Frederick Air Force Base, Oklahoma, which had been abandoned by the Air Force, as had San Marcos Air Force Base, Texas, Stewart Field, near Savannah, Georgia, Childress Air Force Base in Texas, and the Air Bases at Shawnee and El Reno, Oklahoma.

Far down on the list of abandoned, or about to be abandoned military installations, was Camp Rucker, Alabama, twenty miles from still another deserted Air Force Base, Midland Field, Alabama. Fort Rucker was a hastily built (in ninety-days) World War II infantry training camp, located equidistant between Enterprise, Alabama (whose claim to fame is its statue of a boll weevil), and Ozark, Alabama, another sleepy little town with a more practical claim to fame. It had sent to the Congress, until he died in office during World War II, Henry Bascomb Steagall, a powerful, if behind the scenes, Southern Democrat (who was author of the Federal Deposit Insurance Corporation Legislation). Steagall's replacement, George Andrews, was and is a member of the House Military Appropriations Committee. The some-time mayor of Ozark, Banker-Lawyer-Real Estate Broker Philanthropist-James Douglas Brown is a friend of Alabama Senator John Sparkman, Chairman of the Senate Banking and Currency Committee and one-time vice-presidential nominee.

With an absolutely straight face, the Army announced that Camp Rucker had been chosen as the site of the new Aviation School, and cited as about its only reason that Rucker possessed three 5000-foot runways, and had large concrete truck parking areas which could be used as helicopter landing pads.

The runways had been built during World War II as an auxiliary field for the long abandoned Midland Field. They had seen only sporadic use since then.

Testing of Army aircraft had been conducted by the Aviation Test Section of Army Field Forces Board Number One (Artillery), also stationed at Fort Sill. It was transferred to Camp Rucker together with the Aviation School. The authority for the move was a letter from Secretary of the Army Robert T. Stevens on July 23, 1954.

The date, perhaps, is as good as the official birthdate, June 6, 1942, to mark the real beginning of Army Aviation as a major force within the Army, rather than as a specialized service ranking with, for example, the Army Postal Service, Graves Registration, or Special Services. This is not to downgrade these latter three, all important, and perhaps even essential to the Army, but rather to mark the date when Army Aviation became more than a specialized service, and assumed the role, if not the legal status, of a combat arm or technical service.

There had been those in responsible positions who had worked toward the establishment (perhaps re-establishment) of an Army Aviation Corps, a full-fledged branch of service, with its own collar insignia and official heirarchy. This position was voted down by those officers who remembered the difficulties posed by the Army Air Forces when it was technically, but not really, a part of the Army.

If Army Aviation was to truly be of the Army, then it must be truly part of the Army, with its officers and men soldiers first, and aviation technicians second. Almost from the beginning, a program of ground duty was instituted for pilot officers, under which they would periodically return to their parent branch for a year or two of duty as an infantry company commander, or a post signal officer, or in some other, basic

specialty. This was impractical for enlisted specialists, of course, but even today, the collar insignia of aviation enlisted men reflects their origins in the "ground-pounding army" with one crew-chief sergeant wearing the crossed rifles of infantry, the radio technician wearing Signal Corps crossed flags, and the door-gunner on a UH-1D wearing perhaps the crossed pistols of the Military Police, or possibly even the shield of the Adjutant General's Corps.

There were perhaps no more than a hundred "professional" officers in Army Aviation at the time of the establishment of the Aviation School at Fort Rucker. A definition is necessary here: A professional officer is for this purpose defined as an officer who, by virtue of being a West Pointer, or a Regular Army officer from another source, and by virtue of his career to date, can logically hope to wear a colonel's eagle, or the stars of a general.

The comparative handful of "professional" aviation officers had alternated duty as pilots or aviation staff officers with tours as commanding officers of units of their branch, with attendance at branch and higher level schools, such as the Command and General Staff College at Fort Leavenworth, Kansas, and the Armed Forces Staff or War Colleges.

The vast bulk of the officer personnel assigned to aviation, no matter what branch insignia adorned their lapels, were in many cases experienced only in aviation. They had become pilots as lieutenants, and had done nothing but fly, or administer, in aviation activities since. There were artillery majors who had never commanded a battery, infantry lieutenant colonels who had never commanded a platoon, much less a company or battalion, Signal Corps officers who literally did not know an ohm from a watt, and armored officers whose only experience with a tank had been to see one from the air.

Army Aviation, until the establishment of the Aviation School at Fort Rucker had a not entirely undeserved reputation for being sort of a military Siberia. One applied for aviation duty, the morning following the party at which one had insulted the Colonel's lady; once in aviation, return to the Ground Army was difficult if not impossible. There was a certain resentment toward, for example, artillery captains who had never fired a cannon and yet, because of flight pay, were being paid more than artillery majors who had spent their careers in a fire direction center or at the guns.

But the Korean War, and the establishment of an Aviation School and Center in 1955 changed this. Professionals in the Ground Army saw in a Flying Army not only an entirely new, and rather exciting concept of war, but an even greater chance for advancement based on brains and ability.

The not-quite-exalted professional reputation of the Aviation Officer Corps, at the same time, made the establishment concerned with who would lead the new Flying Army. At the same time that the up-coming young officers began to look at aviation with new interest, the establishment greased their paths into it.

Colonel Allen M. Burdett, Jr., is a good case in point. A West Pointer, Burdett had graduated in time to see combat, with distinction, in the Second World War. He had served with greater distinction as an infantry battalion commander in Korea, rising to be a very young lieutenant colonel. His career was assured. Shortly after becoming an extremely young full colonel, he reported to Fort Rucker to learn how to fly. Burdett commanded the 1st Aviation brigade in Vietnam, was later Director of Army Aviation, and at this writing (November 1970) commands Fort Rucker, as a Major General.

To Rucker, too, came Brigadier General Bogardus S. Cairns, who had earned his

Allen M. Burdett, Jr. as a colonel in 1962.
(*U. S. Army*)

Shortly after getting his own wings, Brigadier General Bogardus S. Cairns (left) pinned the first set of Master Army Aviator Wings on Colonel Robert Williams, then president of the Army Aviation Test Board. (*U. S. Army*)

spurs as a tank commander in World War II, and was, perhaps more than any of the others, an unquestioned member of the establishment.

When the Signal Corps established its own aviation test unit at Fort Rucker, to develop an adequate communications and navigations system for Army Aviation, they chose not to name any of the perhaps fifty Signal Corps lieutenant colonels already in aviation to the command. Instead the Signal Corps heirarchy persuaded Lieutenant Colonel Charles A. Merritt, a non-flier, to go to flight school and become the first commander of the Signal Aviation Unit. Merritt's previous career had alternated between classified assignments (he had commanded the mysterious Task Force Able in Korea, a multi-service unit which, among other things, was charged with getting spies back and forth across the North Korean lines) and serving as hatchet-man for the Signal Corps, "visiting" Signal Corps units world-wide to trim the deadwood.

Outstanding younger and far more junior officers throughout the Army were given a word to the wise over a drink at the colonel's house and applied for aviation duty.

There was a great deal of resentment over the newcomers within Army Aviation, as it became painfully obvious that the newcomers were getting the desirable staff and command assignments. Colonel Robert R. Williams, who was named president of the Army Aviation Board, was the aviation establishment's most powerful member. He had been a member of the first handful of officers assigned to aviation in World War II, and had remained with aviation since then. He was a West Pointer. More than anyone else, Williams poured oil on the waters, and reminded all concerned that aviation had more than enough bureaucratic fighting to do as an entity to have time to scrap *en famille*.

The Air Force was already demonstrating that it had had second thoughts about turning over to the Army the responsibility for aviation within one hundred miles of the front lines, and under a certain (5000 pound) gross weight.

The Air Force was also having a battle with the Navy and the Marines over roles and missions, all carried out under the table.

Logically, and perhaps inevitably, the Navy and the Army formed an under-the-table alliance. The Marines, for example, just happened to have some surplus officers, by a great coincidence pilots with great experience with piston-engined aircraft. The Army just happened to have an equivalent number of officer vacancies, and just about a hundred Marines took off their gold wings and put on silver, to finish their uniformed careers as soldiers.

They were generally officers of the quality of Major James Skinner, who, on his retirement as a soldier immediately found work with the Federal Aviation Agency, as an air-crew examiner, testing pilots of airline jets for proficiency. In the just over two years he served as an Army officer, he taught the brand-new senior airmen of Army Aviation everything from the basic techniques of flying twin-engined aircraft to the logistics required to maintain aircraft in remote areas.

When Army planners, seeking ever larger helicopters and fixed-wing aircraft ran into polite, but firm, resistance from their brothers in arms in the Air Force, the Navy proved far more cooperative. The large Sikorsky helicopter program, for example, and the Grumman OV-1 Mohawk program were begun under Navy (or Marine) auspices.

When Fort Rucker turned to the Air Force for transport aircraft, the Air Force replied that they regretted their budget wouldn't allow the assignment of either aircraft or pilots for such an operation, and

An unmarked Navy R4D on loan to the Army on the ramp at Cairns Field, 1957.
(*Author's Collection*)

The Aviation Test Board portion of Cairns Field after the massive infusion of money and effort. Photo taken from a Mohawk at 5000 feet. (*Author's Collection*)

that the Army should apply, through channels, for aircraft whenever they had a specific need for air transport. The Navy was
much more obliging. They happened to have
some surplus R4D aircraft (R4D is the
Navy designation for the Air Force C-47,
Douglas DC-3 Gooney Bird) and some surplus parts for the surplus aircraft, and they
would be very happy in the interests of
economy, to loan these aircraft to the Army.
The ex-Marines were perfectly willing to
teach the Army pilots how to fly the Gooney
Birds, and did.

It must be reported that while the upper
echelon of Army Aviation was engaged in
trying to keep the peace, the lower echelons
found the Air Force attitude annoying.
Army lieutenants wearing the tank and
crossed sabers of Armored as well as pilot's
wings found it amusing to refuel at Maxwell
Field, home of the Air University in Mont-
gomery, because they sensed that a tank
driver flying a Navy airplane turned necks
red in the Air Force.

Very slowly, because anything bureaucratic is slow by definition, and because
there were severe budgetary limitations,
Fort Rucker changed from an infantry
training base into a major air installation.

The influence of John Sparkman in the
Senate and George Andrews on the House
Military Appropriations Committee helped
a good deal. The runways at Ozark Army
Airfield were lengthened and widened, and
additional hangars were built. A large Base
Operations Building was constructed, and
the whole renamed Cairns Army Airfield
in memory of Major General Bogardus S.
Cairns, Rucker's commanding general, who
crashed to his death in his helicopter when
his carburetor iced up.

Another airfield, this one named after
Thaddeus Lowe the balloonist, was constructed on the Rucker reservation to train
fixed-wing pilots. The largest heliport in the
world, Hanchey AAF, was erected at still

Major General Bogardus S. Cairns. His first—
and last—official photograph as major general.
He crashed to his death at the controls of his
H-13 shortly after this picture was taken.
(Fort Rucker, Ala.)

another site, and the countryside, in and
off the reservation, became dotted with dirt
and paved landing strips and helipads.

Colonel Allen Burdett, who had been
flying not quite two years, was named
Chief, Aviation Combat Developments
Office, and the word leaked out that the
Army planned to have an entire division
of troops, 15,000 men strong, trucks, cannon, mess halls, even the chaplain, entirely
movable by organic aircraft.

The Air Force dropped its mask of polite
opposition and howled in outrage. Army
Aviation had spokesmen now, people like
Major General Ernest F. Easterbrook, who
learned to fly and replaced Bogardus
Cairns. Easterbrook was also establishment.
A West Pointer, son of one-time Chief of
Chaplains, he was married to General "Vine-
gar Joe" Stilwell's daughter. He had some

experience in institutional scrapping, too. During World War II, he had been the buffer (formally Inspector General) between the China-Burma-India Theatre Headquarters and the incredibly tough, wholly irreverent toward things military, Merrill's Marauders.

Easterbrook stated his case. So did another brand-new flyer, Major General (later full General) Hamilton H. Howze, the third Cavalry-Armored general by that name. It went up in the military system until it was laid on the desk of Defense Secretary Robert S. McNamara on August 20, 1962.

It is conjecture, of course, to presume that McNamara was aware of the mess the United States was shortly to be in Vietnam, and regarded what the Army proposed as a possible valuable tool in that war. It is a fact that he ordered a board to be formally convened, to test exactly how well the Army could move itself about the battlefield in its own aircraft. Hamilton Howze, recently promoted to the rank of lieutenant general, was named president of the board, and Fort Bragg, North Carolina, was selected as the site for the tests the board would conduct.

The "Howze Board" convened at Fort Bragg, and the word leaked out, long before the official report of the board was declassified, that it had given its blessing to a vastly expanded Army Aviation program.

It was not, however, simply a matter of a group of Army officers sitting around and deciding that they were right all along and had now decided to make it official. Army boards simply don't work that way. While the Army frequently demonstrates a bureaucratic ineptness bordering on the ludicrous, their record for dealing with the basics of the Army is rather good.

The point here is that boards have historically been reluctant, even loathe, to advocate any new tool, or technique of war as the new standard, even when it strikes both casual observer and dedicated proponent as being the obvious thing to do.

The relatively quick, almost total blessing given to Army Aviation by the Howze board must be considered in this context. Only a handful of its most passionate supporters hoped for that much; all were aware of Patton's troubles in the early 1940s of trying to establish an autonomous tank force, and all were aware that what they were trying to sell didn't have nearly as much going for it as Patton's armored force had had.

All Patton had asked for, really, was administrative, as well as tactical control of equipment already in the military system. Everybody admitted that tanks were a good thing. There was by no means such a blanket endorsement of Army Aviation even within the Army. Much of the equipment itself was untested, and had never been used in warfare by us or anyone else. There was serious doubt that the Army could—or should—involve itself in the massive logistical effort an Army Aviation system would require.

In large part, those who watched the Howze board convene thought that, at best, it might result in further action; that the board's report would come out and say something to the effect that there was possibly some merit in the idea of the Army having a larger aviation force than it did at present; that the idea should be developed further; that another board be convened at some later date when more information would be available for its consideration.

Many dedicated believers in the idea that aviation was the key to greater battlefield mobility harbored secret thoughts that the Howze board would agree with this, but come to the conclusion that since it would be such a large effort, that it was properly the function of the Air Force, and that the board report would recommend in effect that the Air Force be directed to provide far greater support at all echelons, and that more effective liaison be established.

There were many who wished that the Howze board hadn't happened, just yet, who felt that Army Aviation would have a greater chance for survival, not to mention expansion, when there had been more time to develop equipment and techniques and tactics. At the moment, many people thought, it was so new and so weak, that cutting it down would be entirely too easy.

Within the Army, there were branch enthusiasts who hoped that the board's actions, acted upon by the Secretary of Defense, would add Army Aviation, or parts of it, to their own baskets of eggs. The Transportation Corps, for example, was a relatively new branch of service. Transportation Corps officers let it be known that since aviation was, more than anything else, a method of transportation, it properly should be a Transportation Corps function, with Helicopter or Fixed Wing Transport Companies performing the same role for the Army as Transportation Truck Companies.

If the Army was to have airplanes, subtly announced the Ordnance Corps, their development and supply should be an Ordnance Corps function, as was the development and procurement for the rest of the Army by the Ordnance Corps of trucks and tanks and weaponry.

There were two arms of the service, one with congressional status (armored) and one without (airborne) who felt that Army Aviation really belonged to them, considering their roles and missions. Armored announced itself to be the arm of mobile warfare, and what could be more mobile than a helicopter or an airplane? Airborne, said airborne, meant just that: "Carried by the air." Perhaps the helicopter would be a far more efficient means of getting an in-

fantry soldier where he was supposed to fight than was the parachute. In any event, airborne authorities announced without much bashfulness, the obvious place for aviation was under airborne doctrinal control.

It may be fairly presumed, too, that the Air Force, while not delighted with the idea of any board not under its control discussing aviation at all, was at the same time rather secure in the belief that first of all the board would not do anything drastic, and that, if the unexpected did happen, they would count on having the ideas shot down by wiser heads in the Department of Defense.

The Howze board report was finally published, given a "secret" security classification, and returned to the Defense Department. Its contents were known throughout the services just about as soon as the pages came off the off-set printing machine. It was an heritical document.

In essence, the Howze board report said that Army Aviation, as an integral part of the Army, could do everything its proponents said it could, and more. It should function more or less like airborne, that is to say, as a way of service, but not as a legal branch of service. It should be under its own chief, and have its own heirarchy. The recommendations and conclusions which were profuse and detailed, boiled down to three major points. First, that the idea was sound, and that further discussion should be limited to not if, but how. Second, that acquisition of equipment and matériel proceed as rapidly as possible, under whatever priorities were necessary, and that, third, plans be immediately started to conduct a divisional level troop test, not, to reiterate, to see if Army Aviation would work, but to detect and eliminate any defects found as the new methodology of war was put into use.

The Air Force swallowed hard and

The first Chinook arrives for the 11th Air Assault Division (Test). The Army smiles, the Navy is tactfully neutral, and the Air Force looks glum. (*Author's Collection*)

awaited Defense Department action on the report. It wasn't long in coming: The 11th Airborne Divison was to be renamed the 11th Air Assault Division (Test) and full-scale testing of the concept of an Airmobile Division was to commence as soon as possible. In the meantime, procurement of equipment, and training of pilots and other personnel was to proceed as if the testing of the airmobile division concept had already proven satisfactory, with changes to be made as the testing showed the need for change.

Long before the testing of the 11th Air Assault Division (Test) was accomplished, everyone involved knew what was going to happen just as soon as the equipment could be obtained, and the personnel trained. There was a sudden massive shuffling of paper, and some hasty redesignation ceremonies.

The 1st Cavalry Division was in Korea. On July 1, 1965, its colors were returned to the United States, and exchanged in a brief ceremony for the colors of the 2nd Infantry Division, based at Fort Benning. The 1st Cavalry troopers in Korea became instant members of the 2nd Infantry Division. The members of the 11th Air Assault Division (Test) became as instantly members of the 1st Cavalry Division (Airmobile) and prepared to go to Vietnam under the command of Major General Harry W. O. Kinnard. The colors of the 11th Air Assault Division (formerly 11th Airborne) was furled and stored in a warehouse.

Table of Organization and Equipment Number 67 was published.

It was quite a document, providing for an Airmobile Division, wholly airmobile, with all of its subordinate units, all of their personnel, and their wealth of equipment. The Division was fighting in Vietnam before the Table of Organization and Equipment had been finally refined and approved.

The Mohawks: Front to rear. OV-1A, OV-1B OV-1C. (*Grumman Aircraft*)

Under a headquarters company, which included three general officers, one colonel, six lieutenant colonels, 38 other officers and 107 enlisted men, there was an MP Company (9 officers, 147 EM), an Aviation Group with 1992 officers and men, a Signal Battalion with 336; an Engineer Battalion with 620; five brigade headquarters each with 213 men; an Air Cavalry Squadron with 770 men; Division Artillery 1848 men strong; a 3195-man Support Command (Supply and Maintenance); 5 standard infantry battalions, each with 767 officers and men, and three infantry battalions, made up of paratroopers, each with 729 men.

In all, there were three generals, seven colonels, 45 lieutenant colonels, 133 majors, 402 captains, 579 lieutenants, 674 Warrant officers, 40 sergeants majors, 194

The Bell HU-1B (now UH-1B). (*Bell Aircraft*)

The Bell HU-1D (now UH-1D). (*Bell Aircraft*)

master sergeants, 479 enlisted men in the E-7 pay grade, either platoon sergeants or technicians receiving the same pay, 957 in grade E-6, 1200 in grade E-5, 79 in E-4 and enough privates to make up an enlisted strength of 11,050 enlisted men and a total divisional strength of 15,847 officers and men.

TOE 67 provided a vast array of equipment. From Item Number 503120, Barber Kit, Complete (111 of them); to eight briefcases, leather, 8×16 inches; to twenty-one Christian Chaplain's flags and ten Jewish Chaplain's flags; forty-eight mimeograph machines of one kind or another; two baritone and five tenor saxophones; and ten vacuum cleaners. There was also provision for three Grumman Mohawk OV-1B airplanes and three OV-1C Mohawks. Five items further down the list of equipment were 111 UH-1B helicopters and 176 UH-1Ds, the larger version of the same machine. Forty-eight huge Sikorsky CH-37 "Mohave" twin-engined helicopters were also provided.

The Airmobile Division immediately proved its worth, even if there was no resounding, total victory over the enemy that most Americans have come to expect. There is little doubt in the mind of any serious student of the military that without the unprecedented, almost unbelievable maneuverability the Airmobile Division possessed, the Vietnamese War would have gone much worse for the United States Army than it has. There has been no Dienbienphu in Indochina for the Americans,

The Sikorsky H-37 Mohave. (*Sikorsky Aircraft*)

Colonel Jack Marinelli, as president of the Aviation Test Board, shows off the Army's first Caribou to the Mayors of Daleville (left) and Enterprise (right), Alabama.

(Collection Col. Marinelli)

and, although the Paris Peace talks have proven useless, the United States did not sit down to them as the French had sat down in Geneva, immediately after having suffered a humiliating defeat on the battlefield.

The Airmobile Division, and the overall air mobility of the U. S. Army in Vietnam, has prevented a defeat.

There was one more political squabble, concerning the De Havilland of Canada's twin-engine transport, the CU-2 Caribou. The Air Force said that the Caribou was obviously a transport airplane and therefore obviously the Air Force's. Their argument was valid, but the political position of the Army, as a result of their success with aviation in Vietnam, was such that a deal, rather than a surrender, was possible.

Colonel Charles A. Merritt, who had gone into aviation in 1957, and who now wore both the star wings of a senior aviator and the Distinguished Flying Cross for his own service in Vietnam, agreed to transfer the Army's inventory of Caribou to the Air Force and the Air Force agreed that in the future the Army would have full and total control of the development of its helicopters. The Army's inventory of Caribou aircraft was transferred to the Air Force on January 1, 1967. While some are still in use by the Air Force, most of them have been "sold" to Air America, which, in probably the worst kept secret of the war, is universally acknowledged to be the air arm of the Central Intelligence Agency. They are in use throughout what used to be Indochina.

NINE

Fixed Wings

THE current Army inventory of aircraft, because of the Vietnam War, is not made public, except by type. There are two fixed-wing observation planes, the O-1 Bird Dog and the OV-1 Mohawk, and they have only their mission in kind.

The O-1 Bird Dog (formerly L-19) is in daily use both in the United States and overseas and by the Air Force and Marines as well as the Army. It is the first aircraft procured specifically for the Army, and it continues to perform the duties for which it was designed. The Army intends to replace it over a period of time with the OH-6 helicopter, the Hughes light observation helicopter.

The O-1 is a two-seater aircraft powered by a 213-HP Continental engine. It has a high wing, a 36-foot wing span and is 25 feet 10 inches long. It cruises at mean sea level at 100 mph, and has a maximum speed of 115 mph. Maximum range is 592 statute miles, and it has an endurance of just over 4.5 hours.

There are several models in current use.

The TO-1D is an instrument trainer version, equipped with a variable pitch propeller, and a complete set of instruments for the rear (passenger/student) seat. The O-1F version is the O-1D without the rear instrument panel, with the ultra-high-frequency communications removed, and with a very-high-frequency (for contact with ground units) radio in its place. The O-1F also has bomb shackles installed in the wings, which are used to carry droppable loads, wire dispensers and the like.

The OV-1 is a twin-engine, highly sophisticated very fast turboprop aircraft whose development and use is a story of its own.

There was a general realization that, simply because war always becomes increasingly complex, a more complex, more "sophisticated" surveillance aircraft would eventually be necessary. This realization, and the official statement of it, is very much like the same sort of statement made with regard to rifles, tanks, and even jeep-type vehicles. There's always room for improvement.

The O-1 formerly L-19). (*Author's Collection*)

The O-1 on water skis. (*Author's Collection*)

The O-1 in Air Force colors.
                (*Author's Collection*)

The Aviation Test Board mounted a turboprop engine in this L-19A for test purposes.
                (*Aviation Test Board*)

In June 1956 the Army's Continental Army Command, approved Type Specification TS 145, which called for the development and procurement of a two place, twin turboprop aircraft designed to operate from small, unimproved fields, sheltered water, mud, snow, and escort carriers, and be capable of performing missions of observation, artillery, and naval gunfire spotting, air control, and emergency rations supply, liaison, and radiological monitoring.

After winning a design competition, the Grumman Aircraft Corporation of Bethpage, Long Island, was designated the prime contractor. The Air Force was charged with providing suitable engines, and for liaison with the engine manufacturer, Lycoming. But the Navy, rather than the Air Force, would have charge of administration. The Navy said they were interested in the airplane because the Marine Corps wanted one like it, and the Marine Air Wing was the Navy's responsibility.

The Army announced that the Signal

Corps would develop, test, and procure the rather elaborate communications, navigations, navigation and surveillance equipment planned for the Mohawk.

When, in March 1957, it was officially announced that Grumman had won the competition to build the new observation plane, Grumman had more than 150 people already at work on the project and had actually built a full-scale, wooden model (a mockup) of the cockpit. A mockup is very much like a full-size model airplane, complete to every possible detail. The human mind, despite its abilities, still finds it much easier to examine a model than to visualize the finished product from engineering drawings.

In September 1957 the mockup board met at the Grumman plant in Bethpage. After examining the mockup, which they found generally satisfactory, the board adjourned. Shortly afterward, the Marine Corps, through the Navy, announced that they were pulling out of the Mohawk program. The Army would continue with it, alone.

In April 1958 the Phase II contract was let, on behalf of the Army. It called for the building and testing of nine aircraft, together with the engineering services required to make the machine work. They were to be called YAO. Y for Prototype, A for Army and O for Observation. The Air Force made grumbling noises about the Army doing it on their own, and announced they were going to closely monitor the whole business. They would have made much louder noise had they been aware of what the Army was doing, under the protective cover of keeping the airplane suitable for Marine use if the Marines should later want the plane.

In each wing, on the combined Marine-Army mockup, there were "store stations." This is essentially a reinforced section of the wing with "hard points" to which

Nineteen 3.5 inch rockets ride in each of these two dispensers hung from a Mohawk wing. In background, an auxiliary fuel tank is fitted to the stores station of another Mohawk.

(*Author's Collection*)

"stores," such as external fuel tanks, parachute pods, or the like may be attached. The like includes pods of machine guns. And bomb racks. And rocket racks. The Army was forbidden to have such things as bombs, or rockets, or machine guns, on its airplanes.

The store stations, except one on each wing (announced to be for external fuel tanks) were covered up, but not eliminated. Beneath the smooth aluminum skin, the reinforced wing sections remained.

The Army announced that it was cheaper to do it this way than to redesign the wing.

There was only major change in design from the first proposed aircraft to the first

A Mohawk OV-1A with the three piece vertical stabilizer. (*Grumman Aircraft*)

built and delivered YAO-1. The original design called for a single, large vertical fin and rudder. Wind tunnel tests, however, showed that it was going to be impossible to trim the Mohawk directionally with the left engine shut down, without resorting to a powered-control system.

This wasn't a satisfactory solution for the Mohawk. In addition to the weight penalty of the hydraulic system, there would also be increased maintenance problems, probable interference with other mechanical and electrical systems already in the stabilizer shaft, and probable longitudinal trim problems when the wing flaps were lowered. The single tail had to go.

It was replaced, after a great deal of engineering effort and wind tunnel experimentation with a triple tail, like that on the Lockheed Constellation, last and fastest of the piston-engined transport planes.

Two Mohawks were built to be systematically wrecked. They were complete airframes, identical to the aircraft which would eventually take to the air, missing only the installed equipment and subsystems. Aircraft development contracts stipulate that no flight test may be accomplished which imposes on the airplane any strain which has not already been applied, statically, to a static and fatigue test airframe. In other words, before a test pilot is permitted to make a dive, the engineers have already determined by applying hydraulic jacks to a wing, that the wing is strong enough to take the stress the dive will apply.

There are two steps to this airframe testing. First, forces equal to one and one half times the stress expected in flight are applied. If the computer reports that a dive at 300 knots will produce pressures of, for example, 100 pounds per square inch on a certain portion of the wing, then jacks will apply 150 pounds to the same portion of the wing. If there is no failure, a pilot then takes the plane aloft and dives at 300 knots.

Eventually, to gather data, pressure is applied statically until the components fail. The structural integrity of the Mohawk's fuel tanks was subjected to another test, beyond the static. Mohawk tanks are a part of the airplane, rather than parts put on it. A separate section of the Mohawk tank section was built, rested against a wall, and fired at with a machine gun.

One of the two static aircraft was loaded with sand and pig iron, to duplicate the weight of engines, instruments and other equipment, and then dropped to test the strength of the landing gear and the effect on the airframe of rough landings.

The Mohawk has a Martin-Baker ejection seat, a device which quite literally shoots the pilot through the roof of the airplane when he pulls a trigger, setting off an explosive charge. With the cockpit of the Mohawk both in front of, and quite close to, the propeller blades, a pilot simply couldn't jump out of the plane with the engines turning, because he would jump right into the propeller disc.

The ejection system had to be tested before the first flight. The forward fuselage section of one of the two static test aircraft was shipped to the Navy's Air Crew Equipment Laboratory in Philadelphia, where the tests were conducted. A Martin-Baker Ejection Seat trainer at the Pensacola Naval Air Station in Florida was made available to train the Army pilots who would fly the first test Mohawks, and Army L-19s soon became a common sight on the Pensacola transient aircraft ramp.

More than thirty major tests were necessary and were performed, and this took almost two full years. One of the requirements established was that the Mohawk have a service life of ten years, at an average of 800 flight hours per year, or 8000 flight hours. Results of metal fatigue tests indicated that the Mohawk would be still safe to fly after twice this anticipated life, or 16,000 hours.

Finally it became time to fly the bird. And very much like the thrilling movies of the early 1940s suggested (generally with Richard Arlen, begoggled, and grim-lipped at the controls) the most critical test was the power dive, technically, "the rolling pull out."

This is not simply a question of gaining altitude, ramming the throttles to the fire wall and pushing the stick forward. It is first necessary to build up to speed, testing the aircraft's controllability and soundness at successively higher speeds.

And going a little further than this, adding to the natural vibrations of high-speed flight, a device called a shaker is installed in the airplane, actually shaking it in flight, trying to cause failure in a situation where the plane can still be saved.

Aviation Test Board test pilots for the Mohawk were headed by Major Bert Drane (center) and civilian Joe Givens, left, shown with Colonel Jack L. Marinelli, then president of the Aviation Test Board.

(Aviation Test Board)

The tests began, and the speed of the dive was increased. It was said of the Grasshoppers that they took off at 40 miles per hour, flew at 50, dived at sixty and landed again at 20. The Mohawk's dive speed passed first 200 mph, then 250, then 300, then 350, and 400.

The top dive speed for the Mohawk was to be 450 miles per hour. Mohawk Number Three went into a dive. Telemetry equipment on the ground indicated when it passed 350, then 400 mph. The speed kept increasing. At 450 mph, the pilot, and the sensors, reported a shaking in the tail structure. At 460 there was, in the euphemistic phrase of the engineers, a component failure induced by vibration.

It was something close to a Richard Arlen thriller: the center fin and rudder flew off. But not neatly. As they tore loose, they slammed into the elevators. The screaming Mohawk suddenly pulled violently out of its dive. The effect was that of nine and one half times the force of gravity.

In the movies, this is where the wings part company with the plane, and the hero's buddy and girl friend look away from where the plane will smash into the earth. But this was a professional test pilot at the controls of the Mohawk, as much engineer as pilot, and he safely (if quickly) landed the machine.

When the Mohawk was examined, both wings were found to be bent permanently out of shape. The fuselage longerons had buckled. It was possible to pick rivets from the skin of the airplane with one's fingers.

The airplane would not fly again, but its telemetry was intact and proved that the Mohawk was a very strong bird indeed. It was equally evident that something had to be done to keep the center fin and rudder attached to the rest of the airplane.

This was easier said than done. After a number of bright ideas had been advanced, and tested, and had failed, a full-size tail section was shipped to the David Taylor Model Basin near Washington where the failure environment was duplicated in a wind funnel.

The fix finally developed for the fluttering tail section was simple. A third hinge was installed between the fixed and movable portions of the stabilizer and weight, all of .6 pound, was added to the rudder tab.

The next YAO-1 on the production line was given the modified tail assembly. It flew beautifully, reaching maximum speed of the aircraft without any difficulty. It was now official. The YAO-1 became the AO-1.

The first Mohawks were distributed to the agencies charged with their testing. At Fort Rucker, for example, as the Army Aviation Board tested the airplane for its practicality as an Army airplane, the Transportation Corps agency at Fort Rucker, TATSA, began a testing program to determine precisely how much of a problem the Mohawk was going to pose for the Army as a logistical item. And, at the same time, the Signal Corps unit, SCATSA, began to test the Mohawk's aviation electronic systems. The Mohawk came into being at just about the same time as the word coined for aviation electronics, *avionics*.

For those who had envisioned the Mohawk as sort of a glorified L-19, an observation airplane in which they could roar and soar, rather than glide and hide, this latter activity, the *avionics configuration of the OV-1* came as something of a surprise. Deaf to the complaints that what they were doing was dirtying up a good airplane, still another brand-new unit, the U. S. Army Combat Surveillance Agency promptly began to load the Mohawk down with an awesome array of avionic equipment. ACSA was charged with developing the new equipment, and SCATSA to see that it worked properly in the airplane. Still another Signal Corps function, the Electronics Proving

A SLAR equipped Mohawk. (*Grumman Aircraft*)

Ground at the old Indian fighting cavalry post at Fort Huachuca, Arizona, was charged with seeing that the surveillance equipment functioned as it was supposed to in a mock combat environment.

There were bugs in the airplane right from the start. The first SCATSA pilot to fly the Mohawk, for example, was retired Major L. L. McCullough working as a civilian. McCullough got no farther than the end of the runway before he had to abort his test. He'd worn out inadequate brakes between the parking spot and the runway.

But there were no major design deficiences that couldn't readily be corrected. The aviation board quickly found out that the Mohawk's steering was inadequate for field use in the Army, which meant operating from dirt strips and crowned country roads. In the soft dirt of rough landing strips, the nose wheel would turn sideward and roll the tire off the rim. On crowned country roads, the Mohawk was uncontrollable, and generally lurched drunkenly into a ditch.

The fix was simple. Power steering was provided for the nose wheel, and the Mohawk proved just as agile in the field as its 40-hp predecessors had been. Other

mechanical problems appeared as TATSA flew round the clock, seven days a week to put a thousand hours of flight time on each of the planes, but these were corrected about as quickly as they were detected.

The Army Combat Surveillance Agency, working with the Signal Corps laboratories at Fort Monmouth, New Jersey, and with the Army Electronic Proving Ground at Fort Huachuca, however, moved somewhat faster in their efforts than the people trying to put the Mohawk into army-wide use. Before the Mohawk was ready for SLAR, SLAR was ready for the Mohawk.

SLAR, which was classified at its inception, stands for Side Looking Airborne Radar. It was a long time before much more than that was declassified. The antenna, a long, squarish oblong hangs from beneath the Mohawk fuselage. It is generally accepted that the radar detects the movement of the enemy as the surveillance aircraft flies along the battlefront, parallel to it. The battlefront of World War II gave way to the Main Line of Resistance, or MLR during the Korean War, and is now officially called FEBA, for Forward Edge, Battle Area.

Since no Mohawks were yet available for testing of the SLAR, a substitute carrier,

Still wearing its VIP paint job and high polish, this L-26 carries a test SLAR antenna on its side. (*Author's Collection*)

or platform, had to be found. In addition to the Beechcraft L-23, the Army had on hand a half-dozen twin-engined Aero Commanders, rather plush, rather fast high-winged aircraft which had been bought "off the shelf" as personnel transports. This translated to mean their assignment as the L-26 (now U-9) to senior officers. The teletype machines one day began to clatter. The aircraft were to be flown immediately to Fort Monmouth or Fort Huachuca, there to be stripped of their plush leather upholstery, there to serve as test beds for Side Looking Airborne Radar. When the L-26s were in too short supply for the entire SLAR testing program, L-23s were requisitioned. There were howls of protest, but the planes went nevertheless.

Meanwhile, Grumman began to construct what are known as the "production aircraft." The first of these, the AO-1AF were very much like the prototype YAO-1s, and could be called refinements of the first test

A Beechcraft L-23D equipped with SLAR being tested in April 1957. (*Beech Aircraft*)

An L-23D with both SLAR (below fuselage) and weather-avoidance radar antennae (in nose). (*Author's Collection*)

aircraft. Larger electrical generators were installed, to meet the greater electrical power requirements of the new avionic equipment, which, in addition to the SLAR, still to be installed, included communications and navigation equipment which would permit Mohawk flight in any kind of weather. Four of the original six stores stations were deleted. An anti-icing system was installed, and the arrangement of the instruments and gauges on the control panel was changed so that it would conform to a standard arrangement of instruments in all Army air-

planes. The nose section, originally riveted in place, was equipped with hinges to provide access to the innards of the instrument panel.

As this was going on, there were frequent, often confusing and even maddening changes directed by one or another of the agencies charged with developing the Mohawk. Some of the equipment the Signal Corps announced would be in the airplane

Another VIP transport (note paint job) put to work as a flying test bed. This aircraft tested a SLAR antennae (below fuselage) developed by the University of Michigan. (*Beech Aircraft*)

A ski-equipped Mohawk. (*Grumman Aircraft*)

was simply not available for installation, or even available as a sample, so the Grumman factory could make provisions for it. And then, the SCATSA test of installation of a new item of avionics often indicated that for either mechanical, electrical, or radiation reasons, an already installed piece of equipment would have to be moved someplace else. Working from blueprints and using black boxes that were just that, black wooden boxes, for samples, Grumman installed shelving and wiring for the equipment that was not yet available. The first eighteen production aircraft were delivered in this condition, and became known as the "Initial A's." The aircraft which would actually have the equipment planned for them were to be known as the "Ultimate A's."

Then a little more information became declassified about SLAR. It wasn't simply a device with a radar scope on which blips appeared. The Radar Reconnaissance Sys-

An unclassified photo of part of the pilot's control panel. This is what the pilot sees to his right. (*Grumman Aircraft*)

tem, AN/APS-94 would do a great deal more. As the Mohawk flies, the radar makes maps of the terrain on either side of its flight path, producing either two continuous 5-inch strip maps, or a single continuous 9-inch strip map. And it does this automatically, within seconds, using a rapid film processing system and 9-inch film. Flying at night, in thick fog, the observer riding in the Mohawk has a second-by-second map of the land to either side of him rolling out of a machine in front of him. At the same time, through a data-link, the same information is being transmitted to another map making device, normally at a ground headquarters, but potentially anywhere. This was to prove extremely valuable in Vietnam.

And as the SLAR function became more generally known, other functions for the Mohawk began to appear. Infrared sensing devices headed the list.

Of the first thirty-five AO-1AF aircraft ordered, seventeen were redesignated as AO-1BF SLAR carriers. As soon as the production line turned out the thirty-fifth aircraft of the initial procurement order, the rumor about infrared became the reality. Production began immediately on a total of forty-two Mohawks, twenty-five "ultimate A's," and seventeen C models. By the time they were completed, we were at war, if unofficially, and production figures remained secret. The theory of infrared sensing devices is common knowledge. *How* the Army's Signal Corps does it is the secret. Radar sends out a pulse, which, on bouncing back to an antenna, signals the presence, or absence, of something on the ground. Infrared, however, is a detection system which uses the radiation generated by any object hotter than the objects around it, from the red hot exhaust of a rocket, or the heat of a cigarette, or even the temperature of a human body.

What had begun in the eyes of most of the old-time Army aviators as a rather snazzy observation airplane, from which they could observe, or photograph, the ground had become in fact a highly sophisticated weapon of war.

It was still possible, of course, to use

A SLAR equipped Mohawk destined for the West German Army. Extra fuel tanks are fitted to the stores stations.

(*Author's Collection*)

the Mohawk as a visual observation plane, and all models of the Mohawk came equipped with the KS-61 camera system. This is in itself a highly efficient, automatic photograph system, far superior to anyone aiming a camera out the window.

A pilot on a photographic mission adjusts a dial on the camera control to correspond to his altitude and speed. Automatically, the speed of the camera is adjusted so that photographs taken overlap and form as long a continuous photograph of the ground as wanted, up to the camera's film magazines' capacity of 250 feet of 19-inch-wide film. At night, the KS-61 automatically fires up to 104 pyrotechnic photoflares, enough for the film available, and timed for perfect exposures.

The camera itself, located in the middle of the fuselage, can be rotated by the pilot to point left, or right; to 15 or 30 degrees oblique, and straight down.

The array of communications, navigation, and identification equipment is both impressive, and for the most part classified.

The Army is reluctant, too, to discuss the subject of armed Mohawks, but some returned Mohawk pilots are more willing. The stores stations, originally built into the aircraft for the Marine's interest were sturdy enough to support rocket launcher pads, and the mounting for the mini-gun, a Gatling-gun type weapon firing up to 6000 rounds per minute.

Somehow, some Mohawks turned up armed "for self-defense" in the Vietnam operation, and proceeded to render more than journeyman service to the ground troops when they were not occupied with their other missions.

The Army Chief of Staff, the story goes, was in Vietnam on an inspection tour when he came across the armed Mohawks. He brought the matter forcibly to the attention of the Vietnam Commander, General William C. Westmoreland, reminding him that

the Army was forbidden to have armed fixed wing aircraft. General Westmoreland first politely inquired that if the Air Force wasn't unhappy about the Mohawks why should the Army be? When the Chief of Staff insisted that it was against Army policy and must be stopped immediately, Westmoreland is reported to have replied that so far as he was concerned, he was commanding a combined forces operation, and that the Mohawks would continue to go armed. The Chief of Staff, if he wanted to, could consider the Mohawks attached to the Air Force or for that matter, to the Republic of Korea's detachment of troops; the guns weren't coming off.

General Westmoreland is now Army Chief of Staff, and, so far as is known, he hasn't mentioned the armed Mohawks to the present Vietnam commander, General Creighton W. Abrams, and the Mohawks are flying armed, even if the Army refuses to admit it publicly.

The number of Mohawks in the Army is classified, and so are the details of the many improvements to the original aircraft. Larger engines have been provided, as well as other technical modifications.

The last published specifications for the aircraft show that it was originally equipped with two Lycoming engines, each developing 1000 shaft hp. With 10-foot diameter three-bladed, fully reversing propellers (which permit the Mohawk to both land and take off in a manner that can only be described as spectacular) the maximum speed was listed at 325 mph with a cruising speed of 207. Without external fuel tanks, the operating range was given as 774 statute miles, and the service ceiling as 33,000 feet. The wing span was 42-feet, the length 41 feet and the height 12 feet 8 inches. Gross weight was 12,675 pounds.

It can be safely assumed that the current Mohawks are faster, heavier, and better all around.

A half-dozen new Mohawks in flight. Specifications classified. (*Author's Collection*)

In the addition to the O-1 Bird dog and the OV-1 Mohawks the Army has a rather vast fleet of other fixed-wing aircraft in its current inventory.

The L-17 Navion, which was used during the Korean War, is no longer around, nor is the LC-126, an off-the-shelf Cessna first purchased during the Korean War. Both were turned over to Army Flying Clubs in the late 1950s and early 1960s. Piper's L-21, of which there were a total of 219, all purchased during the Korean War has similarly been declared obsolete and surplus to the Army's needs and either given away or otherwise disposed of.

In 1958, the Army first experimented with a jet, the Cessna T-37. This was . . . is . . . a two-place aircraft, designed as a trainer, and powered by two small Continental J-69-T-9 turbojets, giving it a max-

imum military power speed of 408 miles per hour. The version tested by the Army at Fort Rucker had a cruise speed of 368 miles per hour, an endurance of 2.8 hours and a range of 796 statute miles.

The Rucker testing, by the Army Aviation Board and the Aviation Combat Developments Agency, indicated that the aircraft was satisfactory as a high-speed observation plane and that it could be supported in the field by Army maintenance units. It offered another ability, that of a weapons platform for use in support of ground troops, but this was a mission forbidden at the time to the Army, and the idea was regarded with amused skepticism by the Air Force. The jets were returned to the Air Force when the tests were completed.

The Air Force today is quite proud of the A-37, in daily use in Vietnam, which is the same machine equipped with rockets, machine guns, and bomb racks, performing the mission the Army said it could perform more than a decade ago.

An even faster, more, in a sense, Air Force Type jet aircraft, the Italian Fiat G-91, was loaned to the Army for test in 1961 by the North Atlantic Treaty Organization. This was a small, single-seater fighter plane with a top speed of 715 miles per hour.

It, too, passed all Army requirements for a high-speed observation airplane, as well as a flying cannon and rocket platform, and there was a good deal of talk within the Army of making an issue of the Fiat, trying to justify its presence with the Army.

The Air Force was on very solid political ground in the matter, however, for the Fiat G-91 was on its face a jet fighter, forbidden to the Army. The matter came to rest once and for all the day the Fiat left Fort Rucker. Making its last takeoff from Cairns Field, with the aircraft designer at the controls, it lost power on takeoff and crashed, killing its designer-pilot.

Transport aircraft were another matter. The Army had bought a large number of De Havilland of Canada Beavers, a six-place, high-wing utility aircraft, starting in 1951. They had been designed for use in the Canadian and Alaska bush country. A radio that would net with Army ground units was fitted, a coat of olive-drab paint applied, the craft designated the L-20 shipped to Korea.

It immediately found a home in the Army. Equipped with several variations of the Pratt & Whitney R-985AN engines, developing 450 hp and a Hamilton Standard two-blade variable-pitch propeller, it was ideally suited to the Korea terrain.

Almost seven hundred Beavers were acquired during and after the Korean War, and, redesignated the U-6, it is in use all over the world today.

The Beaver is 30 feet 4 inches long, and has a wing span of 48 feet. It is 10 feet 5 inches high and weighs, empty 3000 pounds.

Four years after the Beaver was purchased by the Army, De Havilland came up in 1955 with a larger version, the Otter, which is 11 feet 7 inches longer (41 feet, 11 inches) two feet two inches taller (12 feet 7 inches) and has a 10-foot greater wingspan (58 feet). Powered by a 600-hp Pratt & Whitney engine, the Otter (U-1A) is an eleven place aircraft weighing 4431 pounds empty. Its maximum speed is three miles less than the Beaver (156–153) and cruises five miles per hour slower at mean sea level altitudes (125–120). It is the largest and heaviest (maximum gross weight 8000 pounds) single engine utility aircraft in the world, and it, too, immediately found a home in the Army.

It was very much what the Army said it wanted, a battlefield support vehicle, a flying Army truck, simple to maintain, requiring only a single pilot, and adaptable to any number of missions. Transportation Aircraft Companies were formed, under the Transportation Corps, under the command of a captain, and with warrant officer pilots for the Otters. Some of these were among the first Army units to be sent to Vietnam.

The De Havilland L-20 Beaver (now the U-6).
(*De Havilland Aircraft*)

An Air Force Beaver in England. It is the slowest plane in the Air Force.
(*De Havilland Aircraft*)

A Beaver takes off from Tan Son Nhut Airfield, near Saigon. (*U. S. Army, Vietnam*)

A De Havilland aircraft Beaver fitted with a turboprop engine tested by the Army.
(*Army Aviation Test Board*)

The U-1A Otter in Arctic Region paint scheme (red and white). (*De Havilland Aircraft*)

Interior view of the Otter.
(*De Havilland Aircraft*)

An Otter on floats in Alaska.
(*De Havilland Aircraft*)

An Otter in an inflatable portable work hangar in South America. (*Author's Collection*)

The last public listing of numbers of aircraft showed the 255 Otters were carried on the Army inventory. Like the Beaver, they are in use wherever the Army has aircraft around the world, and it is safe to assume that many Otters have been purchased since the Army stopped giving out that kind of information because of the Vietnamese War.

In 1959, four years after the introduction into the Army of the Beaver, the Caribou joined the Army. Built by De Havilland, whose design concepts of aircraft for use in the Arctic and elsewhere meshed very closely with Army requirements, the Caribou is another of the low-, slow-, and reliable aircraft designed to operate from rough landing strips in rough terrain.

Designated the CV-2 after its introduction, the Caribou is a large aircraft by

The original prototype Caribou. Subsequent versions had longer fuselages.
(*De Havilland Aircraft*)

A production model Caribou. (*De Havilland Aircraft*)

A ski-equipped Caribou in Arctic paint scheme in Alaska. (*Defense Department*)

The 1st Aviation Company (Caribou) at Fort
Benning, Georgia, shortly before it went to
Vietnam in 1962. (*Fort Benning*)

Army standards, somewhat larger than the Douglas C-47 with which it is often compared. The wingspan is 95 feet, 8 inches; it is 72 feet 7 inches long and weighs 16,920 empty, and 28,500 pounds loaded. It has two Pratt & Whitney R2000-7M2 engines, each developing 1450 horsepower. At sea level, it cruises at 170 mph, but at 7500 feet, using only 50 percent of its available power, it can cruise at 182 miles per hour, which gives it a maximum range of 1400 miles, which means that the airplane can be flown anywhere in the world under its own power, and with no requirement for added fuel tanks.

The Caribou followed the Beaver and the Otter to Vietnam, where it proved to be a perfectly satisfactory aircraft for its intended purpose and another aviation thorn in the side of the Air Force. The Army bought 173 Caribou in several models.

A turboprop version, called the CV-7

Interior (facing the rear) of Caribou.
(*Author's Collection*)

Buffalo was developed, and four were bought.

This version was much heavier (empty: 22,486) and had a much larger weight-carrying ability (gross weight 41,000, as

Caribou with weather avoidance radar in nose takes off from Tan Son Nhut, Vietnam.
(*U. S. Army, Vietnam*)

Caribou in Vietnamese Highlands. Note length of runway. (*De Havilland Aircraft*)

Vietnamese refugees being loaded aboard Caribou. (*De Havilland Aircraft*)

compared to a Caribou gross weight of 28,500) although only slightly larger. Two GE T-64-10 turboprop engines, developing 2850 shaft hp each made the difference. It was faster (sea level maximum speed is 267 versus 216 for the Caribou; cruise speed at 5000 is 277 miles) than the Caribou but had a much reduced operating range (529 statute miles versus 1400 for the Caribou).

The Caribou and Buffalo were, in fact, transport aircraft of the type restricted to the Air Force and in April 1966, in exchange for a blanket authority to develop all aspects of their own rotary wing aircraft, the Army transferred all Caribou and Buffalo to the Air Force. They are still in use in Vietnam by the Air Force.

Cargo is dragged from rear door by drogue
chute in Vietnam. (*De Havilland Aircraft*)

The Buffalo's maiden flight.

    (*De Havilland Aircraft*)

One of the first Helio Couriers. It had two-
bladed propeller. (*Author's Collection*)

Special Forces Helio Courier makes air drop of supplies. (*Author's Collection*)

The prototype L-23A is given a last ride to the Army Aviation Museum at Fort Rucker in a Caribou. (*Beech Aircraft*)

The L-23B. (*Beech Aircraft*)

The L-23D (U-8D). (*Beech Aircraft*)

The U-8F. (*U. S. Army*)

The Helio Courier has been purchased in limited numbers off the shelf by the Army for use by Special Forces. Designated the OV-10, this is a six-place aircraft powered by a Lycoming GO-480-G1D6 engine of 295 hp. It has huge wing flaps, permitting takeoff and landing from very short, rough fields. It more or less, for the peculiar requirements of Special Forces, fills in between the capabilities of the Beaver which requires both longer takeoff and landing runs, and has a much slower cruise speed (125) than the Courier (164) and the helicopters, which have even slower cruise speeds, although they can, of course, dispense entirely with a runway.

There are probably less than fifty Helio Couriers in the Army, almost entirely within Special Forces.

The first twin-engined airplane in the Army was the Beechcraft Twin-Bonanza, purchased off the shelf, given a coat of GI paint and sent to Korea as the L-23. Between 1952, when the first was bought, and 1965, the Army acquired a total of 206 L-23s, in various models (L-23A, -B, -C and -D). In 1960, a number of the airplanes were equipped with Side Looking Airborne Radar (SLAR-AN-ARQ-86) and designated RL-23D. All of the original L-23A, -B, and -C aircraft still repairable were rebuilt at the Beech facility to be L-23D aircraft. The entire numbering system was changed, and they are now known as U-8D.

They are powered by two Lycoming GSO-480-1 engines which drive them to a maximum speed at mean sea level of 212 mph. At 65 percent of power, they cruise at sea level at 179 mph; at 5000 feet at 187, and at 10,000 feet at 195 mph. They have a range of 1320 miles. Gross weight is 7300 pounds; empty 4978 pounds.

U-8 and U-9 (formerly L-26) aircraft have always been used for the Army equiv-alent of executive or VIP aircraft. Originally, they were more or less the personal transportation of three and four star generals, but as more and more of them came into the Army, their use by lower ranking personnel became more common.

The U-8F is a slightly larger version of the U-8D (two feet longer, 400 pounds heavier at maximum gross weight). It is essentially the military version of the Beechcraft Queenaire. The last public figures showed seventy-one on the Army's supply books.

There is a still another version, the U-21A Ute, powered by two United Aircraft of Canada free shaft turbine engines developing 520 hp each. This aircraft also has a maximum gross weight of 7700 pounds but is designed and intended for use as a small tactical transport. It has a wide rear door to facilitate loading, and is intended to replace, as well as it can, the "lost" Caribou, although the Army officially denies this. In practice, the U-21A is used whenever possible so that it will not be necessary to call on the Air Force for cargo hauls.

In 1965, the Army issued an initial purchase order for fifty-five Beechcraft Barons. This Four place "light-twin" was re-designated the T-42A and put to work as a trainer for instrument flight, and for transition from single to multi-engine flying.

Powered by two Continental IO-470-L engines rated at 260 horsepower, the Baron soon became popular with Army brass because it cruised 23 miles per hour faster than the U-8F (at 5000 feet) and was easier to "justify" (get one) with its four seats than a seven-passenger U-8F. Most of them nevertheless are still officially classified as trainers and stationed at Fort Rucker.

Fort Rucker also has the bulk of the more than 255 Cessna 172s purchased by the

Interior of the U-8F. The pilot is Lieutenant Colonel Jim Lefler, the first twin engine pilot in the Army, just before his retirement.
(*Beech Aircraft*)

The T-42A. (*Beech Aircraft*)

The Army has acquired a number of these World War II vintage C-45s and uses them in the United States. (*U. S. Army*)

The first T-41B (Cessna 172). (*Fort Rucker, Ala.*)

The U-9 (formerly L-26). (*Author's Collection*)

OH-13 in Arctic paint scheme and "bear-paw" skis for use in snow. (*Fort Richardson, Alaska*)

Army starting in 1966. This standard civilian airplane, dubbed the T-41B by the Army, is considerably cheaper to operate than any other aircraft in the Army, and its Army installed, complete set of navigation equipment makes it a splendid, economical training machine.

There are still a few, almost jealously guarded, Aero Commanders around the Army, designated the U-9 (formerly L-26).

This is a five-place high wing twin-engined aircraft capable of cruising at 10,000 feet at 226 mph. In all, the Army purchased twenty of them, in various models. In January 1965, nine remained, scattered all over the United States. There are probably fewer than nine remaining now, but, like the last cavalry horse, this glamour machine of Army Aviation is likely to be around a long time.

TEN

The Choppers

THE Army came out of the Korean War with a relatively few helicopters.

Most common of these was the Bell H-13, still in the inventory as the OH-13.

The first experimental version (called the YR-13) joined up in December 1946. Early versions had the still familiar plastic bubble cockpit, but the aluminum tubing running aft to the tail rotor was covered, sometimes with cloth, other times with aluminum. The covered tail section was uncovered when it proved both unnecessary and even undesirable (as in a strong quartering wind).

There have been YR-13, R-13, H-13, and OH-13 helicopters in many models (-A; -B; -C; -D; -E; -G; -H and -K and S, plus a version called the TH-13). All but the OH-13s and the TH-13 are powered by a convention gasoline piston engine, in several models, developing 250 horsepower. The OH-13s and TH-13 have a more powerful, turbo supercharged engine developing 260 hp. The latter two aircraft have sea level maximum speeds of 105 mph against 81 mph for the older versions, and a 5000 foot cruising speed of 92 mph versus 88.

The last time such figures were available, the Army had purchased a total of 2197 OH-13s in various models; 283 OH-13s and 220 TH-13s.

The OH-23, manufactured by Hiller, bears a strong resemblance to the OH-13. Both have plastic bubble cockpits and exposed frame members. They are both in current service in Vietnam, although in the process of being replaced by new machines as they become available.

The Hiller has a more powerful (305 hp) engine in the OH-23G, but others are equipped with a substantially identical Lycoming engine of the same (250 hp) power as the OH-13. Many Hillers saw service in Korea, and many were used at the Army Primary Helicopter Training Center in Texas.

In 1950, the Army bought four Sikorsky H-18A helicopters, a four place, single-rotor machine with a 33-foot rotor. These were primarily test machines, and no further procurement was made.

The Sikorsky H-19 got in on the closing days of the Korean War (or the opening days of the armistice) and, like the Beaver,

The OH-13S. (*Bell Helicopter*)

The TH-13T. Instrument Trainer.
(*Bell Helicopter*)

An early H-23. The cockpit bubble has a flat
surface. (*Author's Collection*)

A current model OH-23G at Tan Son Nhut, Vietnam. (*U. S. Army, Vietnam*)

Two Sikorsky H-18As. (*Sikorsky Aircraft*)

Firing rockets at Fort Rucker from an H-19 in 1958. (*Fort Rucker, Ala.*)

A rocket firing CH-34 at Fort Bragg, North Carolina, in 1962. (*Fort Bragg, N.C.*)

immediately found wide acceptance at all Army echelons.

It has a single, three-bladed rotary wing with a 53-foot diameter, driven by a gasoline piston engine (either Curtiss-Wright or Lycoming) of 700 hp. It can carry twelve passengers at a maximum sea level speed of 112 mph, and a cruising speed of 91 mph. It has a range of 360 statute miles.

The first procurement order was let in 1949, and between then and the last public figures of 1965, the Army purchased a total of 355 of them, calling them Chickasaws.

Still in the inventory as the UH-19, it is the little brother of the Sikorsky CH-34, which entered the service as the H-34 four years after the UH-19.

This is a sixteen-place helicopter built on the same lines as the UH-19, but larger (rotor span is 56 feet) and more powerful (Curtiss-Wright R-1820-84 piston engine of 1425 hp) and faster (sea level maximum speed is 122 mph; cruising speed 108 mph).

(This is the first helicopter trusted to carry a President of the United States. The Executive Flight detachment, under Lieutenant Colonel William B. Howell, was charged with that responsibility during the Eisenhower administration. Under the Kennedy-Johnson administrations, the Army was relieved of that responsibility by the Marine Corps, although all Presidents since Eisenhower have taken advantage of the convenience of having a helicopter at their disposal.)

The H-34 was redesignated the CH (for cargo) -34 and is still in the active inventory, although generally being replaced by Bell, Vertol, and larger Sikorsky helicopters. The Marine Corps' version of the machine is still the mainstay of the Marine rotary wing fleet in Vietnam.

The CH-34 evolved further into the huge CH-37, the first of which entered the Army in 1956. The rotor diameter of this huge machine is 72 feet. It is powered by two Pratt & Whitney R-2800-54 piston engines developing 2100 hp each. The engines are mounted outside the fuselage in nacelles; the landing gear is retractable. Beneath the cockpit are clamshell doors through which it is possible to drive a jeep and trailer, or a light artillery piece. It will alternatively carry thirty-six troops. It cruises at sea level at 115 mph.

In daily use in Vietnam and elsewhere around the world, the CH-37 Mohave is probably the largest rotary wing aircraft, with a cargo or personnel fuselage, that will ever be built. Experience in combat has shown that it makes far more sense to suspend heavy loads beneath a helicopter than to try to get them inside a fuselage.

The Sikorsky CH-54A evolved from the CH-37. Two Pratt & Whitney JFTD-12A-1 turbine engines each developing 4050 shaft hp each replaced the CH-37 gasoline engines, and the fuselage was more or less simply discarded. The rotor diameter (of a six-blade rotor) was increased to 72 feet.

It can lift more than 20,000 pounds, and both the Army and Sikorsky boast that the huge cost of the flying cranes has been many times recovered in Vietnam. A downed airplane or helicopter, which would otherwise be lost to the enemy, is simply picked up and carried home by the Sky Crane. The last published figures indicated the Army had twenty-eight Sky Cranes; there are doubtless many more than that.

An interesting feature of the machine is that it has an extra set of controls, facing backward, so that during pickup and release operations the pilot can see what he's doing. An aluminum body pod has been developed for the machine, which is capable of carrying sixty-seven troops or forty-eight litters. When the pod, which might be considered a fuselage, is not needed, it is simply left behind and the Sky Crane reverts

A Marine CH-34 supporting the Army's 101st
Airborne Division in Vietnam.
(*U. S. Army, Vietnam*)

The CH-37. (*Author's Collection*)

Servicing the CH-37 at night. (*Author's Collection*)

Loading a "Pershing" missile through the clam-shell doors. (*Author's Collection*)

Three Mojaves above Aschaffenberg, Germany.
(*U. S. Army*)

A CH-47 picks up a T-28 in Vietnam.
(*U. S. Army Photo*)

A CH-54A Sky Crane hauls a disabled Chinook over Vietnam. (*Author's Collection*)

A "passenger pod" carried by a Sky Crane.
(*Author's Collection*)

A portable command post beneath a Sky Crane. (*Sikorsky Aircraft*)

in less than a minute to its basic role as a flying crane.

It is impossible to discuss the development of any helicopters without remembering what Lee S. Johnson, president of Sikorsky Aircraft once said in a speech: "Before Igor Sikorsky flew the VS-300, there was no helicopter industry; afterward, there was."

Starting with that first flying helicopter, the list of Sikorsky firsts is long and unmatched:

On January 3, 1944, the first helicopter mercy mission was flown by Commander Frank A. Erickson of the U. S. Coast Guard. He flew through a snowstorm from New York to Sandy Hook, New Jersey, carrying a load of blood plasma to treat sailors injured in an explosion aboard a destroyer.

The first helicopter put to commercial use was the S-51, the civilian version of the R-5. It was first used for charter work by Helicopter Air Transport of Philadelphia in August 1946.

On October 1, 1947, the first helicopter airmail route was established, using S-51s in the Los Angeles area by Los Angeles Airways. Earlier that year, the S-52, the first production helicopter using all-metal rotor blades was flown. An Air Force S-51 was the first helicopter flown in the Korean War. The S-55 (H-19), the first troop-carrying helicopter, became, in March 1952, the first helicopter certificated by the Federal Government as a commercial transport aircraft, and then, on July 8, 1953, the first helicopter used for commercial, scheduled passenger service. New York Airways instituted scheduled service between New York City and the outlying airfields.

The S-56 (CH-47) was the first twin-engined helicopter. A modified Army-owned H-18 (Sikorsky S-52) was the first turbine-powered helicopter. The list goes on and on, and it is important to remember that Igor I. Sikorsky was personally involved in all these developments.

He didn't give up his official title as "engineering manager" of Sikorsky Aircraft until he finally fell victim to bureaucratic decree about retirement age, and "retired" on May 25, 1957.

He remained officially on the company rolls as an "engineering consultant," but this wasn't a sop to the pride of an old man. In 1957–59 he was frequently at Fort Rucker, as the Army developed techniques to use the machines he had invented.

The Army installed its first automatic stabilization equipment (autopilot) in a well-worn Sikorsky H-34 (tail number 299) assigned to the Army Aviation Board. The installation was performed by technicians of the U. S. Army Signal Aviation Test & Support Activity, directed by Lieutenant (now Colonel) Raymond J. Tourtillott of the Signal Corps, and Charles M. Scott, Jr. of Sperry (himself a reserve officer and helicopter pilot).

On hand to watch it, erect, graying, arms folded over his chest, face thoughtful, crawling in and out of the aircraft with as much ease as any of the young soldiers was Igor Sikorsky, who had once flown the Czar of All the Russias in the *Ilya Murometz,* his contribution to World War I aviation.

In 1960, Tourtillott was sent to visit Army aviation units in Germany in connection with various Sikorsky-built Army helicopters. With him went Sikorsky's son and Tourtillott reported that young Sikorsky spent at least half his time making notes for his father.

Helicopters are now part of life. Igor Sikorsky, in his early eighties still hale and hearty at this writing, has had the unusual privilege of watching his dream become a reality. His contributions to rotary-wing flight, as well as fixed-wing aviation cannot be over stated.

The CH-21. (*Author's Collection*)

The first helicopter coast-to-coast non-stop flight was made by this Aviation Test Board H-21. It was refueled in mid-air by an Otter. (*Author's Collection*)

A 105-mm Howitzer lifted by a CH-21. (*U. S. Army*)

This Air Force YH-16 Piasecki, designed to carry forty passengers, proved to be a failure. Only one was ever made. (*U. S. Air Force*)

The Siebel YH-24. (*U. S. Air Force*)

The American helicopter XH-26 "Jet Jeep." (*U. S. Air Force*)

The Doman H-31. (*Collection Col. C. A. Merritt*)

The H-32. Hiller Hornet. (*Collection Col. C. A. Merritt*)

The Cessna H-41. (*Collection Col. C. A. Merritt*)

The Kaman Air Force H-43 was also tested by
the Army. (*Collection Col. C. A. Merritt*)

In the month (June 1950) that the Korean War broke out, the Army let a purchase contract for a twin-rotor helicopter designed and manufactured by the Piasecki Helicopter Company of Morton, Pennsylvania. It was designated the H-21. Powered by roughly the same engine as the CH-34, the CH-21 has two three-bladed rotors, each with a 44-foot diameter. The Army's official name for it, Shawnee, had to face the opposition of Flying Banana from the rank and file, and as the Flying Banana, the CH-21 saw more combat than any other helicopter until the Huey came along.

The French used it extensively in their North African operations, and it was the French experience with the helicopter's unexpected toughness in combat that is the reason often ascribed to the Howze board's decision that the Army must have the helicopter. It was the first cargo helicopter sent to Vietnam, where its ability to carry twenty troops or twelve litters are often credited with staving off an early defeat along the lines of Dienbienphu.

A smaller version of the H-21, the H-25 was briefly in the Army inventory. Fifty 8-place, 475 hp, 92 mph machines were bought from Piasecki, but later were turned over to the Navy, who used them primarily on aircraft carriers, where they fluttered around during takeoff and landing operations to bail Navy pilots who missed out of the sea.

A number of other helicopters had brief contact with Army Green:

Two H-24s manufactured by the Seibel Helicopter Company, were purchased, and tested for possible use as an aerial ambulance. It had a 130 hp Lycoming engine, a 29-foot diameter rotor and a cruising speed of 58 mph.

In 1952–54, the Army bought five H-26s, a one place observation helicopter from the American Helicopter Company. This had pulsejet engines mounted in the tips of the rotor blades.

The McCulloch Motor Company, best known for industrial gasoline engines, entered the lists with the H-30, a two-place, twin-rotor machine powered by a 200-hp Franklin engine. The Army bought two for testing.

The Army also bought two H-31s, manufactured by the Doman Helicopter Company, an eight-place utility helicopter powered by a 400-hp Lycoming engine. It had a four-bladed wooden main rotor, and was quickly dubbed, because of its shape, the Flying Bedroom.

The H-32 was the Hiller Hornet, a two-man observation machine powered by two ramjet engines in the rotor tips. The Army bought six of these for test.

Cessna entered the H-41 Seneca, a 260-hp, four place helicopter in the competition and sold the Army ten before it was decided it wasn't what the Army needed. The Brantley Helicopter company entered the HO-3, a two-place 162-hp machine which was dubbed the Flying Ice Cream Cone. The Army bought five.

The testing of all these machines operationally (rather than as aircraft as such) soon made it apparent that the Army was going to need three types of helicopters: a small, two- or three-man observation helicopter; an 8–15 place utility helicopter; and a large transport helicopter able to transport, inside the fuselage or suspended beneath it, heavy equipment, such as trucks, artillery pieces, and huge fuel bladders.

The testing of the helicopters as machines, to determine how durable they were, how they could be made more durable, how many spare parts they would require, how to train their mechanics and crewmen was conducted at Fort Rucker by a number of separate agencies.

The Army Aviation Combat Developments Agency determined what an aviation unit should be *able* to do. The Army Aviation School came up with tactics, *how* it would do what it was required to do, and how personnel from pilots to mechanics should be taught their trade. The Army Aviation Board tested specific aircraft to see if they *could* do what they would be expected to do, and what sort of service could be expected from a given aircraft in any situation. Helicopters and aircraft were tested in the Arctic and in the desert, in temperate climates and in the jungles. The Aviation Board tests were extensive and expensive.

The Signal Aviation Test and Support Activity tested the installed electronic equipment to see both if it would work as it was designed to work (and to make it work if necessary) and to see that it was able to be used with ground electronics equipment. The SATSA developed training manuals and repair manuals, telling the technician in the field precisely how, step by step—like the instructions in a Do-It-Yourself-Kit—how electronic equipment should be installed in an aircraft, serviced while in the aircraft, and removed when necessary.

The Transportation Aircraft Test & Support Activity performed essentially the same task for the aircraft as a piece of equipment, testing, evaluation, and modification to insure that the machine could "live" with the Army in the field.

All of this went on simultaneously, and under growing pressure as the Vietnam political situation deteriorated into war.

In the last year of the Korean War, 1953, Army planners came up with what they thought a helicopter to replace the H-13 and H-23 should be. The phrase used is "military characteristics," and it sets forth the size, weight, speed, weight carrying capability, manueverability and other traits of a machine which hasn't even appeared on the drawing boards.

The military characteristics and the an-ticipated number of machines the Army will buy are made available to all the manufacturers of helicopters and to anyone else (McColloch Engine, for example) who possesses, or who can acquire, the facilities necessary to design and manufacture a machine meeting the characteristics.

This is known as the drawing-board stage, and manufacturers generally pay for the design themselves, with the large gold bag of military purchase orders dangling in front of their eyes.

Some manufacturers come to realize that they are unable to go through with the project and drop out after an initial engineering investigation. Others go ahead. The initial engineering work frequently shows that military characteristics are impossible in one area or another, impractical in others, and possible only in a few. This results in the changing of military characteristics, when the Army planners are told they can't have what they would like to have because it simply can't be made, or can be made only at prices placing it outside reality.

The Utility Helicopter Characteristics of 1953 were revised in 1959, partially as a result of initial studies, and partially as a result of the Army's changing its own mind based on its own, and the French, experience with helicopters.

The Bell XH-40 helicopter was a result of the revised Military Characteristics for a Utility Helicopter of 1959. Shortly after joining the service, for testing, it was redesignated the HU-1A, for Helicopter, Utility, Model 1, Modification A.

The Huey was born, and although the Army continued to call it the Iroquois, the Huey it has remained.

The UH-1A soon gave way, after testing at Fort Rucker indicated some changes were necessary and apparent, to the UH-1B. From 1960 to 1965, the Army bought 1306 of them.

The Bell prototype YH-40. From this machine have evolved all the "Huey" series helicopters. (*Author's Collection*)

Powered by a Lycoming T-53-L-11 turbine engine developing 1100 shaft hp. It has a maximum sea level speed of 138 mph, a cruising speed of 124 mph and a range of 312 statute miles.

The engine drives a single, two-bladed main rotor with a 44-foot diameter. The helicopter carries a pilot and nine passengers, although Vietnam experience quickly showed that a co-pilot was going to be necessary during all operations, which reduced the passenger load to eight.

The HU-1B (later redesignated UH-1B) is 12 feet 8 inches high; 53 feet long, overall (including rotor arc) and has a 42 foot 7 inch fuselage. It has an empty weight of 4523 pounds and a gross weight of 8500.

Purchased as a utility helicopter, it quickly proved able to function as a light cargo helicopter. For a number of reasons, including performance and a lower rate of maintenance per hour of light than the CH-34, it was decided to both utilize the UH-1B as an interim cargo helicopter and to develop a larger version with greater carrying ability.

There was limited production of a UH-1C and next came the UH-1D which saw the weight-carrying ability increased to twelve to fifteen troops, instead of eight, the normal gross weight upped to 9500 pounds from 8500 pounds, and a larger door installed.

The diameter of the rotor was increased to 48-feet, which provided greater maneuverability and a new more powerful engine (Lycoming T53L-11 developing 1100 hp) installed.

Colonel Jack L. Marinelli leaves an early UH-1A at Fort Worth, Texas, after setting a world's helicopter speed record over a 500-km course on July 23, 1960.

(*Collection Col. Jack L. Marinelli*)

An UH-1A, armed with two .30-caliber machine guns and sixteen 2.75 inch rockets in action at Korat, Thailand, August 13, 1962.

(*Fort Shafter, Hawaii*)

A "slick" UH-1B in Arctic area color scheme. (*Defense Department*)

The UH-1D. (*Author's Collection*)

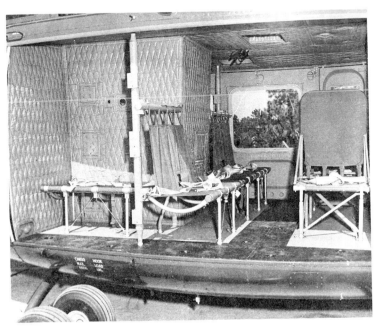

Cargo compartment of the UH-1D. (*Bell Helicopter Co.*)

An UH-1B Gunship in Vietnam. This ship carries two 7.62 mm machine guns and six 2.75 inch rockets on each side. (*U. S. Army*)

An UH-1B fires a French SS-11 wire guided anti-tank missile. (*U. S. Army*)

An UH-1D "Slick" on a supply mission in the Mekong Delta. (*U. S. Army, Vietnam*)

An UH-1B armed with rockets only. This ship
carries a 36-rocket launcher on each side.
(Fort Bragg, N.C.)

The HueyCobra AH-1G. *(Bell Helicopter)*

Pilot's cockpit in rear of HueyCobra.
(*Bell Helicopter*)

Gunners' cockpit, forward, in HueyCobra.
(*Bell Helicopter*)

Left to right Bell's OH-13, AH-1G and UH-1D helicopters. (*Bell Helicopter*)

The Marine Corps version—the UH-1E.
(*Bell Helicopter*)

West Germany bought more than four hundred slightly modified UH-1Ds for their Army, Navy, and Air Force. (*Bell Helicopter*)

The first Chinook CH-47A stopped at the Pentagon on December 20, 1962, en route to Fort Rucker. (*U. S. Army*)

In Vietnam, the UH-1B became a "gunship," equipped with machine guns and rockets and flown as protection for the UH-1D, which (although armed with machine guns in the doors) was used as a cargo/personnel transport, called a "slick" by its users.

The gunship concept, of having armed helicopters accompany and support the transport helicopters proved to be a sound tactical idea. The UH-1B, while it could accomplish this mission, wasn't ideal, so Bell, without waiting for official approval, and at its own expense, developed a pure gunship.

Using the same 1400 hp engine as the UH-1H and the 44-foot rotor of the UH-1C, as well as most other parts, the gunship had only a two-man fuselage, 35-inches wide at its widest point. The crew was to be a pilot and a gunner.

The Army saw the machine in operation and bought it, naming it the AH-1G, Assault Helicopter-Model One, Modification G. It gave up trying to make the Army call the Huey the Iroquois on this model, which is officially known as the HueyCobra.

It carries an impressive array of armament, ranging from machine guns firing 6000 rounds per minute to grenade launch-

A production Chinook CH-47B.
(*Author's Collection*)

ers to aerial rockets. Its speed and performance are classified, but there is no question that the top speed, using the same engine as the bulky fuselaged UH-1D to power a machine with a two-man fuselage 35-inches wide is considerably faster and more manueverable. Its pilots regard it with great affection, and there is considerable competition to become a HueyCobra pilot.

No production figures on either the UH-1D the UH-1H (powered by a T53-L-13 engine, developing 1400 hp) or the HueyCobra are available.

To replace the CH-34 Sikorsky and CH-21 Piasecki-Vertol Flying Banana, the Army gave a development contract to Vertol, which had become a division of Boeing Aircraft. The result is the CH-47 series, the Chinooks, one of the few Army-Indian names that seems to have stuck.

The CH-47A is powered by two Lycoming T-55-1-L-7 engines, developing 2650 shaft hp each. The engines drive two three-bladed rotors, each with a 59-foot-inch diameter. The fuselage is 51 feet long, and the over-all length 83 feet. It is 18 feet 6 inches high and weighs 17,913 pounds empty. Maximum gross weight was listed at 33,000 pounds, but Vietnam experience soon showed that the Chinook could be successfully flown at a gross weight of 38,550 pounds. The helicopter is capable of picking up a field artillery cannon, its crew, and a basic load of ammunition from one mountaintop and flying a hundred miles or more to deposit them on another mountaintop. Before the Army stopped releasing figures, they had purchased 198 CH-47As.

There have been two subsequent models of the CH-47, the -B and the -C.

The CH-47B has more powerful engines, developing 2650 shaft hp (versus 2650) has twin rotors each with a 60-foot diameter (versus 59 feet 1 inch) and, because of the longer blades, an over-all length just shy (99.17) of 100 feet. It weighs 19,375 pounds and has a 40,000 pound maximum gross weight. (Versus 17,913 and 38,500, respectively.) Specifications of the CH-47C are classified, but its generally known that it will have more powerful engines, as well as other improvements.

Except for range, the CH-47 series helicopters seem to have a curious similarity to the C-47 airplane of World War II. Their weight and speed are close, they are designed to carry cargo, and they have proved extremely reliable. The venerable C-47 was pressed into duty in Vietnam as a gunship, with three 6000 round-per-minute guns installed. The Army installed a similar weapons system in the CH-47, firing the Gatling guns out the rear door of the aircraft.

The Chinook had a tragic chapter in its testing. The requirement for it in Vietnam was urgent, and the Aviation Test Board was quite literally flying it round the clock to detect any design or structural failures.

One sunny Alabama afternoon, Mrs. Jane Crawford came to my door in Ozark, Alabama, to tell me that she had just heard over the radio that a Chinook had gone down, and all aboard had been killed. Lieutenant Colonel Chester Crawford was at that time a test pilot flying the Chinook, and she feared the worst. Crawford had already had his fair share of brushes with death. An infantry officer, he had been among the first handful of soldiers sent to the Korean War from Japan, and the only officer or non-com in his unit not to be killed or wounded. She told me she had called Fort Rucker, and they had been unwilling to give out the names of the dead.

I called the pilot's lounge and another Chinook test pilot answered the phone. He was a retired paratrooper who had made five combat jumps before going to flight school. He had gone to work as an Army civilian employee after his retirement from the service.

"Mac, Jane's with me," I said. "Was that Chet?"

He shouldn't have told me, of course, for I no longer had any connection with Army aviation except friendship, but Mac and I had done a lot of things together, and there was another reason.

A World War II vintage AC-47 rigged as a flying gun platform. Each of these 7.62-mm machine guns can fire 6000 rounds per minute. (*Defense Department*)

A Vietnam war vintage CH-47 rigged as a gun platform. A 20-mm machine cannon fires out the rear door. There is a 6,000 RPM 7.62-mm mini-gun mounted outside on each side, and standard 7.62 machine guns in two windows on each side. (*Author's Collection*)

The Chinook floats. (*Author's Collection*)

A skyful of Chinooks. (*Author's Collection*)

Unloading a Chinook in Vietnam. (*U. S. Army, Vietnam*)

"It wasn't Chet," he said. "It was Dick Daniel." He added: "The tail rotor came off; they were at 1,500 feet. There's not much left."

I hung up and told Jane that her husband was all right. Then, because I could not find my voice, I pointed at my neighbor's house where my four-year-old was playing with the three-year-old namesake of Richard I. Daniel.

Mrs. Crawford and I were paying a casual social call on twenty-year-old Martha Daniel when the official notification team arrived from Fort Rucker to tell her that her husband had, together with a Canadian Army pilot on duty with the U. S. Army and a sergeant crew chief, crashed to his death.

It had been said in many quarters of the Army that they were pushing the Chinook too hard in its testing program, that they were trying to cut test and development time too shortly. As soon as the word of Dick Daniel's fatal crash reached the upper echelons of the Army, all Chinooks were grounded, pending a detailed review. Talk was heard of canceling the entire program.

Colonel Charles Merritt, the former Signal Corps hatchet man, was confident that the review would not see the Chinook dropped, but he was equally confident that while the review board met and held its discussions, a good deal of valuable time would be lost in the testing program. He was absolutely convinced that the accident had been just that, an accident, and not a result of a design or structural failure of the Chinook.

"Besides," he said, "I'm already on orders to Vietnam. What can they do to me?"

He waited until he was the ranking man at the Aviation Test Board, during the temporary absence of the two officers senior to him, and then, with a volunteer as co-pilot, he went out to the flight line, and, on his own authority and his own responsibility, cranked up a test Chinook and took off. By the time his superiors returned, by the time he was, in other words, caught at it, Merritt and other volunteer test pilots had flown Chinooks more than a hundred hours. They had proved beyond argument that the machine was sound, and that Daniels accident was a freak that should not be allowed to halt, or even slow, the test program.

The cause of the accident was finally determined to be an improperly installed bolt, worth about thirty-five cents.

Merritt went to Vietnam shortly afterward, not as an aviator, but in his original technical specialty, communications expert. He was given the Legion of Merit for his services as Signal Officer, II Field Force. He was also given the Distinguished Flying Cross for service, in his off-duty hours, as a volunteer Huey pilot. Most of the Huey pilots were warrant officers barely out of— or still in—their teens. Merritt became known as "Uncle Charley," the oldest, highest-paid warrant officer in Vietnam.

He returned safely, and was subsequently retired. Colonel Crawford retired, too, but did not give up flying. He went to work as a civilian, flying Hueys from the factory in Texas to the West Coast, where they would be shipped to Vietnam. One day in 1968, Chet Crawford flew his Huey into the Rocky Mountains. He left a widow and two children.

As the Army sought larger helicopters, they also sought lighter ones, to function primarily as observation platforms, and it was often said that the ultimate idea was to provide an aerial observation platform down to the company level.

A competition was announced for an LOH (Light Observation Helicopter) and two famous competitors began to work on designing and building one. Bell came out with the OH-4, a four-place, 2573-pound

Left to right, the Bell OH-4, the Hiller OH-5, and the Hughes OH-6. (*Author's Collection*)

The Hughes TH-55A. (*Author's Collection*)

gross-weight single-rotor machine powered by an Allison T63 turbine engine developing 250 shaft hp. Using an Allison T63-A-5 turbine of the same horsepower, Hiller Aircraft came out with the OH-5, with the same general characteristics.

At the last moment, a newcomer in Army Aviation, if not in aviation generally, was heard from. The Aircraft Division, Hughes Tool Company, entered the OH-6.

Hughes had been experimenting with helicopters for some time, and had had a good deal of success with a helicopter they had designed for the civilian market. This was a small, almost tiny machine powered by a Lycoming piston engine developing

The first flight of the Hughes OH-6A. Feb. 27, 1963. (*Hughes Aircraft*)

The OH-6A in flight. (*Author's Collection*)

180 hp. It had a rotor diameter of 25 feet 3.5 inches and a gross weight of 1600 pounds . . . only 592 pounds more than the empty weight of 1008. It had a speed (86 mph at sea level) about that of the H-13 and H-23, and about the same range and endurance, but cost nowhere near as much money to operate and maintain.

It was ideally suited to be a trainer, and when the Army saw it, they recognized its virtues as an economical trainer and issued a purchase order for (through 1965) 257 Hughes, which were given the nomenclature TH-55A.

This seemed to whet Hughes's appetite for a larger slice of the helicopter business, and they set out after the OH Competition with an enthusiasm no one else seemed to think was at all justified. Bell and Hiller had all the experience, it was said, and Hughes really had no chance, against all that expertise.

Hughes ran away with the competition in just about every category of specification. In the spring of 1966, the OH-6A set twenty-three world's records for helicopters, including one of a 2215 mile non-stop flight (without refueling) from Los Angeles to Daytona Beach.

Using the same engine as the Hiller OH-5A, but incorporating a much "cleaner" aerodynamic profile, the OH-6A is very fast. Its maximum speed at sea level is 143 mph. The Bell OH-4 has a maximum speed of 135, and the Hiller 128. But the Bell's cruise speed is only 111 and the Hiller's about the same. The Hughes cruises at the same speed as its maximum speed.

The Army issued an initial production order for 714 of the Hughes OH-6A, and it is generally believed that more were purchased. Then, on a re-order recently, Hughes decided that it had to have more money for the OH-6A, and the Army decided it didn't have the money, and the facts seem to suggest that a different, Bell helicopter will replace the OH-6A in the Army. The OH-6A has proven itself in Vietnam, both as an observation helicopter and as sort of a mini-gunship.

ELEVEN

Vietnam

Americans are used to wars where there is a front line; where there are rivers to cross; cities to capture or liberate; a recognizable army representing a government both of which we are determined to destroy.

Vietnam isn't like that. Although it seems quite clear that a nation which could bring Japan to its knees after throwing the Germans out of France could very easily march on Hanoi, it is equally clear that such a course of action has never been seriously considered.

The over-all war is different from any other war we have ever fought. But to the men fighting that war, it is still the rudimentary business of killing, or being killed, of losing life or limb, of individual valor, of self-sacrifice.

Perhaps the best way to tell the story of Army aviation in Vietnam is by telling some of the stories of the valor of individual members of our Flying Army:

Gary George Wetzel was born September 29, 1947, to Mr. and Mrs. George Wetzel of 3910 East Elm Street, Oak Creek, Wisconsin. He went through Oak Creek High School and, on February 15, 1966, entered the Army at Milwaukee, Wisconsin, aged eighteen years and five months.

The Army sent him to Fort Knox, Kentucky, for basic training, which lasted until May 1966 and then to Fort Leonard Wood, Missouri, for training as a clerk. He had a leave home after he finished the school at Fort Leonard Wood and then was flown to Vietnam, arriving there in August 1966.

From August to October, he was assigned to the 383rd Quartermaster Detachment, but he didn't like the assignment and was transferred in October 1966 to the 148th Ordnance Company, where he remained for five months, until March 1967.

He was then transferred to the 173rd Assault Helicopter Company, 11th Combat Aviation Battalion, as a door gunner. Door gunners are volunteers, but they draw flight pay and this has a certain fascination for young men.

Gary Wetzel has freckles, wiry hair, a dimple in his chin, sideburns, and his right eyebrow seems raised in question.

On January 8, 1968, Gary Wetzel, by then a Pfc, was serving as a door gunner aboard a UH-1D involved in a combat assault near Ap Dong An.

The North Vietnamese were waiting for them. The landing zone was brought under heavy fire from both automatic weapons and Russian rockets. Wetzel's pilot was struck and Wetzel left his machine gun to see how he could help.

Two Russian rockets hit the helicopter, tearing it up and throwing Wetzel out of the fuselage onto the ground. He didn't lose consciousness. He saw that he was wounded in his right arm, his chest, and his left leg. His left arm had been blown off.

He made it back to his shattered helicopter, to his door gun and opened fire with it, with just his remaining hand and arm. His was the only weapon then in use. He sprayed the enemy positions with machine-gun fire, destroying the enemy rocket and machine-gun positions which had downed his helicopter and torn off his arm. He remained at his gun until there was no more enemy fire.

Then he tried again to help his wounded aircraft commander. He passed out from loss of blood, regained consciousness, and then, with his remaining arm, helped the helicopter crew chief drag the wounded pilot to the safety of a ricefield dike.

He was evacuated by helicopter first to the 93rd Evacuation Hospital in Vietnam, then to the 249th General Hospital in Japan and finally to the Fitzsimons General Hospital in Denver, Colorado.

The Army promoted him to Specialist Four and the President of the United States, in the name of Congress, hung the Medal of Honor, on its blueribbon, around his neck at the White House.

Specialist 4 Gary Wetzel has also been awarded the Air Medal with twelve Oak Leaf Clusters (signifying second and third awards and so on) the Purple Heart, the National Defense Service Medal and several Vietnamese government awards, as well as the wings of an aircraft crewman.

Frederick Edgar Ferguson of El Centro, California, joined the Army six months after Gary Wetzel, but he wasn't exactly a rookie. Ferguson had done a four-year hitch (1958–62) in the Navy, after graduating from the Phoenix Union High School in Phoenix, Arizona.

He didn't particularly like the life of an enlisted man in the Navy, so he took his release from active service in 1962, and then, two years later, his discharge from the Naval Reserve when he became eligible for it. Almost two years later, in July 1966, he joined the Army Reserve and a month later went on active duty at Fort Wolters, Texas, as a Warrant Officer Candidate.

Ferguson went through the basic flight program at Wolters and then was transferred to Fort Rucker, Alabama, the Army Aviation Center, for transition into the Bell Huey-series helicopters. In May 1967, Ferguson was named an Army aviator and a warrant officer (junior grade), given a leave home (his parents, Mr. and Mrs. Fred H. Ferguson now lived at 1075 Hamilton Street, El Centro, California) and flown to Vietnam, where he was assigned to Company C, 227th Aviation Battalion, 1st Cavalry Division (Airmobile) as a Huey pilot.

Seven months later, the North Vietnamese launched their attack on Hué, the ancient capital of Vietnam. Ferguson, who had by then been promoted to chief warrant officer, was flying a resupply UH-1D helicopter on the outskirts of the city, which was in enemy hands.

On the emergency frequency of his aircraft radio, he heard two messages. The first was a call for help. Another Huey, with a full load of Americans aboard, had been shot down, just outside the enemy's lines. There were wounded aboard who needed help. The second message was an official warning, from someone whose unpleasant task it is to make decisions like this, that the volume of enemy antiaircraft fire in the vicinity of the downed helicopter was such that all Army aircraft were ordered to stay clear of the area.

Ferguson elected to ignore the warning. He dropped the nose of his Huey to pick up all possible speed and then dropped the aircraft to just a few feet off the water of the Perfume River. He flew the gauntlet of enemy fire, literally feet from the muzzles of the enemies weapons. When the enemy saw that his obvious intentions were, to rescue the personnel of the shotdown helicopter, they opened fire with machine guns and mortars on the only place he possibly could land.

The landing site was immediately covered with a large cloud of dust from the exploding mortars and Ferguson had to land under the most harrowing conditions, flying practically blind and under heavy mortar and machine-gun fire. His aircraft was seriously damaged in the process and was unsafe to fly.

Once the rescued wounded were loaded aboard his aircraft, it was necessary for Warrant Officer Ferguson to fly back through the gauntlet of fire, even more severe now as more of the enemy became aware of the only path he could possibly follow.

Chief Warrant Officer Frederick E. Ferguson also received, in the name of the Congress and the American people, the Medal of Honor, from the hands of the President of the United States. He had also been awarded the Distinguished Flying Cross, the Bronze Star Medal, with Valor Device, the Air Medal with Valor Device and thirty-seven Oak Leaf Clusters, as well as the Vietnamese government's Gallantry Cross with Silver Star and other decorations.

Specialist 4 Gary G. Wetzel. (*U. S. Army*)

The third Army airman to win "for conspicuous gallantry and intrepidity at the risk of life above and beyond the call of duty" the Medal of Honor, is a professional soldier, who always wanted to be a career officer.

Patrick H. Brady was born October 1, 1936, at Philip, South Dakota, and was graduated from Seattle University, Washington, in 1959. He was an ROTC student and given a commission as a second lieutenant in the Army Reserve on March 20, 1959. He entered on active duty on April 8, 1959, and almost immediately applied for a Regular Army commission, which was granted on September 17, 1959.

Brady was commissioned into the Medical Service Corps and his lapel insignia has the traditional medical profession caduceus, with the letters MSC superimposed on it. Members of the Medical Service Corps are

Chief Warrant Officer Frederick E. Ferguson.
(*U. S. Army*)

the administrators of Army Medicine, the officers who relieve the doctors of administrative chores.

After a four-month basic course at the Army Medical Service School at Fort Sam Houston, Texas, Brady was sent to Germany, where he served with the 3rd Battle Group, 6th Infantry until March 1961. From that date, until October 1963 he served in an administrative post with the 279th Station Hospital in Germany.

In June 1963 he reported to the Primary Helicopter School at Fort Wolters for basic flight training. In December 1963, a rated helicopter pilot, he was sent to the 57th Medical Detachment, U. S. Army Pacific and then he was returned to the United States in January 1965, to Fort Benning, where he was assigned to the 11th Medical Battalion of the 11th Air Assault Division, during the time that unit (which was later redesignated the 1st Cavalry Division, Airmobile) was being tested by the Army.

In November 1965 he was assigned to the 54th Medical Detachment at Fort Benning and went with it when the unit was assigned to Vietnam.

On January 6, 1968, Brady, by then a major, was flying a UH-1H ambulance helicopter near Chu Lai, South Vietnam. A call for a medical evacuation helicopter came to pick up wounded men from a site in enemy-held territory. It was to be a volunteer mission, for the site was both under heavy fire and shrouded with fog.

Brady found the site by flying up a valley trail and by tilting his helicopter on its side to blow away the fog with the downwash from his rotor blades. As the fog was dissipated, the helicopter became visible to the enemy, who brought it under heavy machine-gun and other small arms fire. Brady successfully evacuated two seriously wounded South Vietnamese soldiers from the site.

Immediately afterward, although his helicopter had been damaged by the first evacuation mission, Brady flew four times to a site where American wounded lay 50 meters from the enemy and where enemy fire was such that two previous helicopters attempting a pick-up had been shot down and others had been chased away by the intensity of enemy fire.

After Brady's four successful flights into the mouths of the enemy's weapons, his helicopter was unflyable and he crawled into another.

As soon as he was in the air, he received news of still more Americans surrounded by the enemy, who requested aerial evacuation of their wounded. He went to get them and did, although enemy fire badly damaged his aircraft and partially shot away his controls as he made his landing. Another helicopter was not immediately available when Brady unloaded his first batch of wounded, so he returned to the surrounded Americans flying the badly shot up helicopter. His second rescue mission was also a success, but when he landed the helicopter at the hospital, it would never fly again.

In a third helicopter, Brady took to the air again and this time the call for help came from an American platoon leader who had wandered with his men into an enemy mine field and was trapped there. Without hesitation, Brady found the field and landed. A mine went off, wounding his two crew members and seriously damaging the helicopter. Brady nevertheless loaded six severely wounded Americans into his aircraft and flew them to medical facilities. The third helicopter would not fly again, either, after it touched down at the hospital.

Brady was told that no more helicopters were available. There may not have been. It may also be that someone felt that a man who, in rescuing fifty-one seriously wounded men, most of whom would otherwise have perished and who had three helicopters shot out from beneath him in the process, had done enough for his country and his fellow man in one day.

Major Patrick H. Brady received his Medal of Honor from the President of the United States with his wife Nancy Lee and his sons Shaun Michael and Casey Leo watching. He has also been awarded the Distinguished Service Cross, with one Oak Leaf Cluster; the Distinguished Flying Cross, (with five Oak Leaf Clusters); the Bronze Star with V device and Oak Leaf Cluster, the Air Medal with forty-two Oak Leaf Clusters, the Purple Heart, the Commendation Medal, and others.

The Medal of Honor, commonly and incorrectly called the "Congressional Medal" is the nation's highest award for valor. Some of our more famous heroes, General Patton, for example (General Patton the elder, it should be specified, now that his son

Major Patrick H. Brady. (*U. S. Army*)

George, who in 1970 became an aviator, is also a general officer) never won the Medal of Honor.

Patton took great pride and justifiably so, in the Distinguished Service Cross, which he received twice. This is the nation's second highest award for gallantry and valor "above and beyond the call of duty." It is awarded to soldiers whose valor often suggests they too should have had the Medal of Honor and many soldiers who receive the Distinguished Service Cross were indeed recommended by their superiors for the Medal of Honor and given the DSC for reasons "the recommending officer" would bitterly challenge.

The citation accompanying the award of the Distinguished Service Cross to Chief Warrant Officer Jerome R. Daly, of Philadelphia is perhaps typical of the level of valor demonstrated by those who have earned the DSC as Army aviators.

Captain Jerome R. Daly, then a warrant officer. (*Courtesy Lt. Col. R. Joe Rogers*)

Daly, now thirty-eight, is a professional soldier-pilot. He holds a bachelor's degree in political science from St. Joseph's College in Philadelphia and was among the first chopper pilots to go to Vietnam. He has more than 5000 hours in the air, half of it as pilot of a gun ship. He was on his second tour in Vietnam when he earned this Distinguished Service Cross:

AWARD OF THE DISTINGUISHED SERVICE CROSS

JEROME R. DALY, W2215549, Chief Warrant Officer, United States Army, 121st Assault Helicopter Company, 13th Combat Aviation Battalion, 1st Aviation Brigade, APO 96307.

Chief Warrant Officer Daly distinguished himself by exceptionally valorous actions on 26 March 1967 while serving as commander of a smoke dispensing helicopter during the rescue of three downed helicopter crews that were threatened by two Viet Cong battalions near Vinh Long. Three helicopters had been shot down in the contested landing zone and all rescue attempts had been thwarted by intense enemy fire from fortified emplacements in a treeline 100 meters from the aircraft. Although it was imperative to rescue the men before nightfall, ground armor reinforcing units were unable to reach the besieged men in time. It was decided that Warrant Officer Daly's aircraft would place a smoke screen between the insurgents and the rescue aircraft. Although he knew that he would be required to fly less than 100 meters from a treeline which contained incredible Viet Cong firepower, he readily gave his consent to the plan. With the pickup aircraft right behind him, Warrant Officer Daly descended, flew in front of Viet Cong automatic weapons and concealed the rescue operation with thick smoke. Although the pickup operations were expected to last a very short time, the downed men were spread throughout the landing area and more evacuation aircraft were needed. Unhesitatingly, Warrant Officer Daly circled and once again placed a smoke screen while passing through the hail of enemy fire. By the time all of the men had been recovered from the field, he had placed himself before the enemy weapons twelve times. Although he and his crew escaped unscathed, his aircraft was so damaged that it was judged beyond repair. Chief Warrant Officer Daly's extraordinary heroism and devotion to duty were in keeping with the highest traditions of the military service and reflect credit upon himself, his unit, and the United States Army.

Daly, who is now a captain, is one of fifty-three officers who have won the Distinguished Service Cross as aviators in Vietnam:

Major C. S. Kettles, Field Artillery
Major General J. J. Tolson
Captain J. A. Scott III., Field Artillery
Captain J. R. Daly, Infantry
Chief Warrant Officer M. L. Mark
Captain R. L. Grof, Armor
Captain R. A. Sperling, Infantry
Chief Warrant Officer W. I. Silverstein
First Lieutenant J. W. Thurman, Field Artillery
Major N. M. Bissell, Infantry
Lieutenant Colonel R. T. Nutter, Infantry
Major J. Toomepuu, Infantry
Chief Warrant Officer P. C. Hopkins
Captain F. H. Mayer, Field Artillery
First Lieutenant A. A. Cozzalio, Armor

Chief Warrant Officer G. N. Terry
Captain K. E. Rubin, Armor
Captain D. R. Vaughn, Infantry
Captain R. M. Breed, Armor
Lieutenant Colonel P. N. Delaven,
Transportation Corps
Major J. C. Bahnsen, Artillery
Captain R. C. Knight, Infantry
Major G. D. Burrow, Artillery
Major T. H. Harvey, Artillery
Chief Warrant Officer J. E. Grimmer
Lieutenant Colonel J. T. Dempsey, Infantry
Major G. D. Burrow, Infantry
Captain R. R. Raw, Infantry
Colonel E. M. Lynch, Infantry
Chief Warrant Officer W. M. Rickman
Lieutenant Colonel W. F. Honeycutt, Infantry
Major C. J. Banks, Infantry
Major R. K. Miller, Infantry
Chief Warrant Officer R. A. Kerns
Major J. H. Patterson, Armor
Captain B. J. Basley, Infantry
Major D. E. Moore, Medical Service Corps
Captain J. J. Boyington, Infantry
Captain T. M. Reeves, Transportation Corps
Chief Warrant Officer K. R. Borck
Major H. E. Stewart, Field Artillery
Major A. A. Rider, Artillery
Lieutenant Colonel M. J. Brady,
Field Artillery
First Lieutenant R. C. Peda, Infantry
Captain C. L. Deibert, Infantry
First Lieutenant J. P. Simons, Artillery
Captain L. G. K. Chock, Signal Corps
Captain P. L. Haley, Artillery
Major P. H. Brady, Medical Service Corps
Warrant Officer Junior Grade L. S. McKibben
Captain B. J. Docey, Artillery
Warrant Officer Junior Grade J. B. Tasker

The Distinguished Flying Cross is awarded to airmen—both Air Force and Army—who distinguish themselves in aerial flight. It is not necessary that the outstanding flying be performed in time of war—explorers and test pilots are sometimes given the award when this country is not at war—but wartime, when safety regulations sometimes must be ignored, sees far more aviators qualifying for the decoration.

Clifford Merritt Walker, Jr. is of old Ala-

bama farmer stock. His family has farmed land in the black belt, north of Selma, since the land was owned by the Indians. His father, as Walker grew up, also farmed a huge wheat farm in Montana, and Walker grew up in an environment of heavy farm equipment and hard work.

He wanted to be a soldier, and he didn't think he wanted to be a farmer. He was graduated from Alabama Polytechnic Institute (now Auburn University) in 1958 with both a degree as an electrical engineer, and a Regular Army commission (he was a distinguished ROTC graduate) in the Signal Corps. As soon as he went into the Army, he applied for flight school, and, still a second lieutenant, graduated as a rotary-wing aviator at Fort Rucker.

His first assignment was unusual for a second lieutenant fresh from flight school. New, junior aviators normally do a tour with a unit in the field, a tactical unit. Walker, however, was an electrical engineer as well as a new pilot, and Colonel Charles A. Merritt's U. S. Army Signal Aviation Test & Support Activity had a high personnel priority. Walker was assigned to USASATSA as a flying engineer just about the time the first prototype HU-1 series helicopters, then still known as the YH-40, came out of the Bell factory and were sent for testing to the Army Aviation Board and USASATSA.

Walker was one of the first handful of aviators qualified to fly the Huey, and he has since flown it about 4000 hours, including more than 1000 hours in combat.

After his USASATSA assignment at Fort Rucker, he was sent to Germany, where because he was one of the few pilots with any Huey time, he spent long hours teaching other pilots to fly the new helicopter.

On his first Vietnam tour, he flew transport versions of the Huey, and then commanded a section, then a platoon, of gunships flying out of Pleiku. Then he was

Major Clifford M. Walker, Jr., (right) his Expert Combat Infantry Badge proudly worn above his Aviator's Wings, received his first Distinguished Flying Cross from General James H. Polk, Commander in Chief, U. S. Army, Europe and Seventh Army, at Augsburg, Germany. (*Courtesy Mrs. Rose Walker*)

given an unusual flying assignment: Special Forces was sending out long-range patrols in search of the enemy. Hopefully, they would not be detected by the enemy deep in enemy territory, for these were small teams, hopelessly outnumbered by the Viet Cong and North Vietnamese. When they were detected, they radioed for "evacuation."

Walker, by then a captain, made the "evacuation" and "withdrawal" flights. This was a precision operation, first by finding the surrounded Special Forces team by means of infrequent radio transmissions and then by picking them up. (The Vietcong and North Vietnamese had radio direction finders, too, and used them to direct fire on the transmitter; the briefer the transmission, in other words, the better.)

Special Forces teams operated in terrain,

both jungle and mountain-jungle, which, while it made them hard to find, also made landing to pick them up difficult if not impossible. Frequently, the evacuations were accomplished by hovering the helicopter over the jungle canopy and dropping a hoist, or a nylon ladder, onto the ground, and picking the men up that way. The enemy, of course, brought the helicopter under fire during the pick-up, while the helicopter, hovering, was in its most vulnerable condition. Among pilots, missions of this type were described as having a "high pucker factor," an apt, if somewhat blunt reference to the sphincter muscles.

Walker flew these high pucker factor missions with such skill that Special Forces paid him a high compliment. They somehow saw to it that he was awarded the Expert Combat Infantryman's badge, an almost unheard of award for a Signal Corps pilot.

When his first tour was over, without any time in the United States, he was sent back to Germany, where he served as a standardization pilot for the Seventh Army, training and certifying other pilots to be instructor pilots. While at Augsburg, the Army gave him more formal recognition than the Combat Infantry Badge for his piloting skill. The four-star general who was Commander in Chief, U. S. Army, Europe, James H. Polk, came to Augsburg and presented Walker, by now a major, with his first Distinguished Flying Cross.

Shortly afterward, Clifford M. Walker, III, was born, and shortly after that, Walker was ordered back to Vietnam. His first assignment was as standardization pilot for the 101st Airborne Division (now really an airmobile division in the pattern of the 1st Cavalry Division, Airmobile).

During the monsoon season, which brings with it dense fog, medical evacuation helicopters were grounded by weather. Three critically wounded Americans in the Au Shau Valley were apparently not going to get the immediate medical evacuation necessary to save their lives.

A pilot with a Special Instrument Certificate, the highest pilot qualification, does not have to ask "clearance permission." It is left to his judgment whether or not it is safe to fly. Major Walker, possessor of a Special Instrument Certificate, fired up a Huey, and took off through the zero-zero weather on his own clearance.

At about 6000 feet, he broke out of the fog. By radio, he contacted the Air Force, who located him on their radar and directed him over the Au Shau Valley. The fog there, which pilots call "the weather" reached to 9000 feet.

Next, Walker contacted the Artillery Fire Direction Center on the ground, and asked for illuminating rounds to be fired at maximum altitude. An artillery illuminating round is an artillery shell, which, rather than an explosive charge, contains a magnesium flare and a parachute. When the shell explodes, the flare, burning brilliantly for about three minutes, floats beneath a parachute.

Walker watched as the shell exploded, and the parachute came out, and the flare ignited. He watched it disappear into the soup, and decided that there was enough glare for him to follow it for several hundred yards in the fog.

Observers on the ground, too, could tell, within two or three hundred yards, where the flare was with respect to their position.

Walker ordered more illuminating rounds to be fired at regular intervals, dipped the nose of the helicopter, and entered the fog banks. He was still on radar guidance from the Air Force, but that didn't last long. Radar works only on line-of-sight, and as he dropped between the mountains on each side of the valley, he lost "line-of-sight," and there came the message:

"Army six-one-seven, we're getting clutter. We're losing you. Six-one-seven, we no longer have you on our screen."

"Six-one-seven," Walker called back, "Roger. Understand. One-seven making descent through the soup."

He was now flying blind, with only his instruments and the glow of parachute flares to guide him, plus the voices from the ground:

"Approximately six hundred yards to our north," the ground would report. It is difficult to estimate accurately the position of a parachute flare in broad day light. Through fog, it is next to impossible.

Walker flew as close to the detonating position of the shells as he dared, which, of course, increased the danger that his ship would be hit by one of the shells as it soared upward. He flew, in dense fog, around the descending flares, in the hope that if the valley wall was somewhere beside him, the parachute flare would hit it before his helicopter struck it.

In this manner, he reached the narrow valley floor. The critically wounded Americans were loaded aboard the helicopter. He lined the helicopter up with a map of the valley, so that his nose was pointed down the valley, and then took off again, disappearing into the fog fifty feet off the ground. Flying now only with instruments, he took off so as to rise as nearly vertical as possible (a perfectly vertical ascent is, especially at the altitudes and the atmospheric conditions of the valley, virtually impossible) as quickly as possible.

It was the most difficult attitude of helicopter flight, but, at 6000 feet, finally, ten minutes later, came the welcome words over the radio:

"Army six-one-seven, this is Air Force Radar Control. We have you on our screen. Take up a heading of zero-five-four for Cam Ranh Bay."

Major Clifford Merritt Walker, Jr. re-ceived his second Distinguished Flying Cross for this mission.

Shortly before his second Vietnam tour was over, he was riding in the left (or co-pilot's) seat of an HU-1D Huey, flying as instructor pilot with another pilot at the controls. A second helicopter, carrying the commanding officer of the one of the 101st Division's battalions was shot down by enemy ground fire nearby. The pilot managed to land the damaged Huey without injury to his passengers, but they were in imminent danger of being overrun by the North Vietnamese.

Walker's pilot flew over the crash site to see of what assistance he could be. The downed Huey had crashed in a wide thicket of tall, relatively young pine trees, too high for Walker's machine to hover above them and pull them out by cable.

Walker had experience, with Special Forces, in getting people out of hairy situations like this one.

He told the pilot that if he was willing to take the chance, he thought he could get to the surrounded men on the ground by using the Huey's rotor blades as a giant, airborne buzz saw, literally chopping them down. Walker was junior to the pilot, but after a moment's thought, the pilot made an exaggerated gesture of taking his hands off the controls, the familiar signal of "You've got it."

Walker edged his helicopter into the pine thicket, literally an inch or so at a time, nose down, watching the edge of the rotor cone approach the trees. The helicopter shuddered as the blades struck the trees, and neatly sliced them off. For five minutes, Walker turned his helicopter into a saw as he hacked out from the pine thicket enough space to get the helicopter within six feet of the ground.

Finally, they were low enough to the ground for a sergeant in the rear of the machine to step onto the landing skid, and then stretch his hand to the waiting Americans on the ground, and to haul them, one by one into the Huey.

Now it was a question of backing out from the area into which he had chewed his way with his rotor blades. With only inches to spare between trees of a size which would smash his rotor blades, he made it.

Before he touched down again, Major Walker had been awarded his third Distinguished Flying Cross, following a procedure known as "impact" awarding of medals when heroic action comes to the personal attention of senior officers. The medal is awarded on the spot, and the paperwork catches up with it later.

Impact awards are always brought immediately to the attention of the next superior headquarters to that making the award. When Walker's impact DFC reached the Field Force Commander's desk, he telephoned to the 101st Airmobile Division Commander for more details.

Major General John K. Wright was commander of the 101st at that time. Wright is not only one of the Army's brighter generals, but a warrior of almost incredible experience. During World War II, when Corregidor, the American fortress in Manila Bay finally fell to the Japanese, the last round fired in its defense came from "Battery Wright," commanded by Lieutenant John K. Wright.

He endured a long and horrible period of confinement as a prisoner of war of the Japanese, and was liberated in Korea when the war was over. Five years later, a very young colonel, he was back in Korea, commanding an infantry regiment with great distinction during the Korean War. Between the Korean War and the Vietnamese War, he rose to major general, and had been,

before coming to Vietnam, Commandant of the Infantry School at Fort Benning.

The conversation between General Wright and the Field Force Commander, concerning Walker's impact award of the DFC, went something like this:

"About this man Walker you gave the DFC to?"

"Yes, sir?"

"How come the other pilot wasn't put in for a medal?"

"He just went along for the ride, sir."

"He could have been left behind then? He could have been landed somewhere while Walker stuck his neck out like that?"

"I suppose so, sir."

"Then why did he go in? Didn't he know what he was getting into?"

"He figured he might be able to help."

"And you don't think that earns him a medal?"

"No, sir, I don't."

"Well, I do, General," the Field Force Commander said, overriding him. "Will you give me his name and rank, please?"

"If you insist, sir. The pilot from whom Major Walker took over was Wright, John K. Major General."

And so Major General John K. Wright, firer of the last round in the Defense of Corregidor, Japanese prisoner of war, Infantry Regimental Commander, Airmobile Division Commander, and Senior U. S. Army Aviator, holder of a Special Instrument Certificate, received the Distinguished Flying Cross to add to his many other citations for valor above and beyond the call of duty.

So many Distinguished Flying Crosses, each awarded for an action like these, have been awarded to Army airmen, pilots, and crew members, that the Army admits it cannot come up with a comprehensive list of them.

TWELVE

Fort Rucker

THERE is little resemblance between the Camp Rucker of 1954 and the Fort Rucker of today. The sleepy little collection of run-down buildings outside the gate is now the town of Daleville, complete to mayor and city council, a large motel, and a huge housing development.

Lister Army Hospital, a new and shining facility named in honor of the Army surgeon who invented the canvas lister bag used for holding chemically treated drinking water, has replaced the World War II jumble of frame buildings. Many troops are quartered in three-story masonry barracks, and more are under construction to replace the remaining rows of frame barracks. A luxurious officers club, an even larger NCO Club, two golf courses, tennis courts, a skeet range, a hunter's clubhouse, motion picture theaters, a sprawling enlisted and officer dependent housing areas of attractive one-story, masonry and frame buildings, and ultra modern classrooms have an air of permanence.

The Aviation Board now occupies two large masonry office buildings and several hangars at what was once Ozark Army Airfield, and which is now Cairns Army Airfield, the second or third or fourth (depending on the training load) busiest airport in the nation. It is a completely equipped airfield, with radar and an instrument-landing system, and a tower staffed by both Army and civilian employees of the Federal Aviation Agency. The sound of aircraft engines, piston, turbine and jet is always in the air, and, at night, the flashing navigation and warning lights of helicopters presents an almost psychedelic display of moving colored lights visible nowhere else in the world.

There is even a museum, connected with the Smithsonian Institution, whose curator, Lieutenant Colonel William B. Howell, Ret., was President Eisenhower's personal helicopter pilot.

Officially, Fort Rucker is the Army Aviation Center. Its commander, a major general, is both Commanding General of Fort Rucker and the Army Aviation Center,

A portion of Fort Rucker from the air. (*Author's Collection*)

The Operations Building at Cairns Army Airfield, Alabama. (*Fort Rucker, Ala.*)

and Commandant of the Army Aviation School. While not the largest school in the Army, it is beyond question, the most expensive, and perhaps the most important.

The Army's concept of having the bulk of its pilots warrant officers has proven sound. Most of the pilots in the Army are warrant officers, who began to train as warrant officer candidates.

The program is open to all enlisted men of the Army meeting certain basic physical and intelligence qualifications. It is possible to enlist directly into the Army for the warrant officer program, and draftees and enlisted men alike are made aware of the program shortly after taking the oath of enlistment.

Roughly, the qualifications are a splendid physical condition, perfect eyesight, hearing, peripheral vision, coordination, and an intelligence level (determined by the standard Army tests given all enlisted men) about that required to enter Officer Candidate School.

Most Warrant Officer Candidates (WOCs) are in their teens, and the Army spends a good deal of time reminding them that they're not old enough to drink. Many young warrant officers go to Vietnam, serve with distinction, and return with a chestful of medals still legally teen-agers, which poses a number of problems for the bartenders at the officer's club.

There are four phases of the training of a young soldier fresh from basic training to be a warrant officer pilot. The first three phases, twenty-eight-weeks in all, are conducted at the Army Primary Helicopter School at Fort Wolters, Texas.

Phase I is sort of a combined Ground School, physical training period, and Officer Candidate School. While many WOCs are fresh from basic training, there are others fresh from Vietnam where they have served in combat (often as gunners or mechanics) and have acquired a sleeveful of stripes

and a practical knowledge of the Army. Phase I makes all of them into a common denominator, a WOC at the lowest level of training.

On entering Phase I, enlisted men below grade E-5 are given a temporary promotion to that pay grade, to last until they are either graduated or dropped from the program. Non-coms and technicians above the grade of E-5 don't lose any pay, but they lose the prerogatives of their rank, and take off their chevrons.

A large number of non-coms used to giving orders and receiving the privileges of a sergeant took one look at what was expected of them during Phase I had second thoughts, and submitted their resignations from the program. The Army had second thoughts, too, and in the belief that a man who had been a good sergeant was likely to be a good warrant officer, refused to accept resignations during the first four weeks, Phase I, of the training.

A Warrant Officer Candidate (WOC) undergoes inspection during the initial, military, phase of his training at Fort Wolters, Texas.
(*Fort Wolters, Texas*)

WOCS marching to the flight line. (*Fort Wolters, Texas*)

The resignations dropped, and the sergeants went on through the program.

While the idea (taking enlisted men, teaching them to fly, and then making them officers when they are qualified) was taken from the aviation cadet program of the Air Corps during World War II, the Army has wisely dropped all hazing aspects of the program.

Advanced candidates are given, so far as junior candidates are concerned, the status of an officer, and are called "sir" and saluted and so on, but there is absolutely none of the nonsense of the aviation cadets such as bracing, shining floors with tooth brushes and so on. The disciplinary measures for candidates accused of hazing are listed together with serious military offenses, and there is no hazing.

The philosophy is that the mission of the training is to teach responsibility, not Prussian-type discipline, and it has been an unquestioned success. This is not to suggest any laxity in discipline or dress, but rather that the WOCs are treated very much as if they were already officers and gentlemen, rather than as some subnormal creature aspiring to that status.

They are housed two or three to a room equipped with desks and chairs, rather than in a typical enlisted barracks. They are rotated in positions of command within their company, and are rated by one another, as well as a commissioned "tactical" officer on how well they perform their duties. It is significant that one of the characteristics rated is "tact."

When Phase I is over, a very few WOCs are sent to Fort Stewart, Georgia, for training as fixed-wing aviators. The bulk remain at Fort Wolters to begin Phase II, Primary Flying Techniques. Phase II lasts just over sixteen weeks and it is here that the WOC is taught, physically, to fly.

A flight Instructor and a WOC pre-flight a Hughes TH-55A at Fort Wolters.
(*Fort Wolters, Texas*)

Part of the Wolters training fleet at Downing Army Heliport. (*Fort Wolters, Texas*)

This WOC wears cap wings signifying he has soloed. (*Fort Wolters, Texas*)

The Hiller TH-55A is the training helicopter, and the training is conducted by
civilian pilots working for a civilian firm
under contract to the Army. The term is
technically correct, but somewhat mislead-
ing, for a substantial percentage of the
"civilian" instructor pilots are either retired
Army or other service aviators, or former
service helicopter pilots, many of them
Wolters graduates themselves.

Periodic check rides are conducted by
active service pilots, and before a student
is turned loose to solo, he receives a final
military-pilot check ride. Once soloed, he is
thrown into the Fort Wolters swimming pool
fully clothed, and thereafter permitted to.
wear WOC (not army aviator) wings on his
cap.

In Phase II, the WOC is also taught
navigation techniques, radio procedures,
and the other basics of helicopter flying,
all in the light TH-55A Hughes helicopter.

Phase III and Phase IV are conducted at
Fort Rucker. Here, the WOCs are housed
in masonry barracks, differing from Bachelor Officers' Quarters only in that they are
somewhat more brightly shined. They are
treated, by and large, very much like officer students, although they are required
to march to mess, and to class, where the
officers are permitted to saunter under
their own power. They are permitted passes
at night, to live with their families if they
are married, and to have their automobiles
with them.

Phase III, lasting a day more than eight
weeks, is the period in which they are
trained in the use of a helicopter in the
field, under tactical instrument conditions.
It is basically a refinement of the basic
flying skills they learned at Fort Wolters.

Phase IV is the training in the use of the
UH-1 (Huey) helicopter. Part of it is spent
in learning how to fly the machine by itself, a transitional training from the
TH-55A, and part of it is the operational

A WOC at the controls of a UH-1B at Fort
Rucker. (*Fort Rucker, Ala.*)

use of the helicopter, which consists in the
main of participating in simulated helicopter assaults, and other mass operations. In
Phase IV, depending on both the requirements placed on the school, and individual
student aptitude, a number of students are
given more extensive gunnery training, at
either Fort Rucker or at Fort Stewart, Georgia. Very few, if any helicopter students go
directly to flying the HueyCobra, this duty
being reserved, if unofficially, for more experienced pilots, more or less as a reward
for past service, or a sop for a second or
third tour in Vietnam.

During Phase IV, too, the student learns
how to fly the UH-1 on instruments, rather
than by visual contact with the ground.
This is considerably more difficult to do in a
helicopter than in a fixed-wing aircraft, be-

Upper, Army Aviator Wings, awarded all who complete flight training. Lower, Senior Army Aviator wings, awarded to Army pilots who have flown at least 1500 hours in seven years. (*U. S. Army*)

Army aviator, with the Military Occupational Speciality 100B, Helicopter Pilot, Utility and Light Cargo, Single Rotor.

As soon as he's had a leave, he's on a jet to fly in Vietnam.

Normally, it is not until after a warrant officer pilot has completed a tour of duty—thirteen months—in Vietnam that he is selected to attend other flight-training programs, such as, for example, that leading to rating as a pilot of the twin-rotor Chinook cargo helicopter, or CH-37 Mohave or the Flying Crane.

Those few Warrant Officer Candidates selected for initial training as fixed wing aviators (fewer because there are proportionately less fixed wing aircraft than helicopters) first attend the four-week Phase One training at Fort Wolters, and then move to

Master Army Aviator Wings. Awarded to Army pilots who possess fifteen years flying experience, 3000 hours of pilot time, and are qualified to fly both fixed and rotary wing aircraft, at least one on instruments. This is the top Army pilot rating. (*U. S. Army*)

cause a helicopter must be "flown" all the time, where a properly trimmed fixed-wing aircraft can be flown "hands-off" and will maintain its course, attitude and altitude for long periods. Colonel Raymond J. Tourtillott, an Army aviator who is both a fixed- and rotary-wing pilot, aptly describes helicopter flight as a "continuous controlled crash" and the fact is that so far as pilot technique is concerned, it is more difficult to teach a man to fly a helicopter than it was to teach a World War II aviation cadet to fly a fighter plane. Flying a helicopter by making reference only to mechanical instrument dials on the control panel is infinitely more difficult than any other flying technique.

On graduation day, with about 150 hours of flight behind him, the Warrant Officer Candidate is given the rank of Warrant Officer, Junior Grade, and designated an

The wings awarded enlisted crew members. (*Fort Rucker, Ala.*)

The T-41A (Cessna 172). (*Author's Collection*)

Fort Stewart, Georgia for primary fixed wing flight training.

The first fifty hours of flight training is conducted in the T-41, the Cessna 172 in Army drab. This is to learn the basic mechanical skills of flying. Phase II, still in the T-41, is another 37.5 hours of instruction, polishing the techniques learned before and after solo flight in Phase I.

Phase III and Phase IV take place at Fort Rucker. First the student is given transition training in the T-42 (the Beech Baron) and then taught to fly the aircraft on instruments. Sixty hours in the air are required, in Phase III.

Phase IV involves sixty-nine hours in the air in the O-1, the single engine Birddog. Forty hours are devoted to learning to fly the machine, and thirty to flying it in a

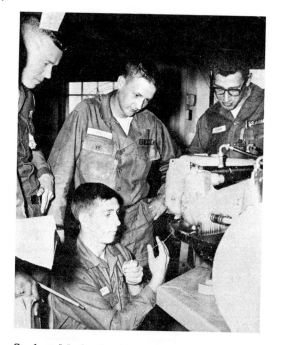

Student Mechanics in class.

(*Fort Rucker, Ala.*)

Major General John J. Tolson III with Alabama Governor George C. Wallace as Wallace congratulates Sergeant First Class Richard Silva at a Fort Rucker decorations ceremony. (*Fort Rucker, Ala.*)

tactical role, observing artillery, operating from dirt strips and the like.

The WOC is given his rating as a warrant officer and designated a fixed wing aviator with a dual rating and an instrument rating. The new fixed wing warrant officer pilot meets the new rotary wing warrant officer pilot on the plane on the way to Tan Son Nhut, outside Saigon.

Commissioned officers, and a rare technician already a warrant officer are given the identical training as their warrant officer candidate counterparts, except, of course, they attend the course as officers,

and do not undergo the four-week Phase I training at Fort Wolters.

Although most newly rated commissioned fixed-wing pilots go to Vietnam with the newly rated warrant officers, from time to time some are sent to the special course for qualification in the Mohawk, but this transition course, as others leading to qualification in the U-8 series aircraft normally come only after a Vietnam tour.

A very few officers and warrant officers succeed in applying for, and getting, training making them both fixed and rotary wing aviators, but courses for this purpose

General Hamilton H. Howze, U. S. Army, as Commander in Chief, United Nations Command; Commander, U. S. Forces in Korea; and Commanding General, U. S. Eighth Army, in 1963. (*U. S. Army Photograph*)

(making chopper pilots from fixed wing, and the reverse) are also held at Fort Rucker.

The top qualification course for Army pilots, leading to certification as an instrument pilot examiner, are also held at Fort Rucker. Each instrument rated aviator (and there are several categories, the top of which is the "Green Card" or Special Instrument Certification, which permits the holder to decide for himself, rather than seek permission from the Base Operation Officer, if the weather is safe enough for him to take off) must take an annual in-flight, and written, examination. The instrument examiners, generally the cream of those holding the Special Instrument Certification, conduct the examinations. Major John D. Roberts, who was the first man to fire a rocket from a helicopter, and who had flown thousands of hours in all areas of the world in all types of army aircraft before his retirement said the instrument examiner course was the only course of instruction he'd ever undergone that he felt he was going to fail, and had been more than pleasantly surprised when he hadn't.

The Aviation School, either at Fort Rucker, or at a subordinate installation, also trains door gunners, crew chiefs, and mechanics, and training of other mechanics is accomplished at the Transportation Corps School at Fort Eustis, Virginia. Signal Corps technicians are trained at Fort Monmouth, New Jersey, and at the Southeast Signal School at Fort Gordon, Georgia.

A newly rated warrant officer in Vietnam can more or less expect to do a full tour at the controls of either a Huey or a Bird-dog. The warrant-officer pilot can look forward on his return to the United States to duty either as an instructor pilot, or with a troop unit based in the United States or elsewhere overseas. He can expect to learn to fly and be assigned to fly the larger cargo helicopters, or, for a fixed-wing pilot, to be trained as a Mohawk or U-8 pilot.

Commissioned pilots can expect the same sort of varied flight training, and, in addition, stand a slightly better chance to learn how to fly both types of aircraft. Commissioned officers, as they are promoted, can also expect to command an aviation unit. The largest pure aviation unit in the Army is the 1st Aviation Brigade, which is commanded by a brigadier general.

The XVIII Airborne Corps is at this writing commanded by Lieutenant General John J. Tolson III, a veteran aviator whose career in the air began as a World War II paratrooper, and who later commanded the 1st Cavalry Division (Airmobile) in Vietnam. The senior officer so far to wear aviator's wings is four-star General Hamilton H. Howze, now retired.

There doesn't seem to be any question whatever that Army Aviation will continue to grow in importance. The war in Vietnam, whatever else it has cost, has given the United States Army a capability in mobility by air possessed by no other nation.

Where it will go precisely is at best a guess, but the odds are that Hamilton Howze, cavalryman, tanker, aviator, will not be the last man in the Army to wear both four stars and silver wings.

EPILOGUE

"Commence the Assault"

THE commander of Operation Nancy Jane has been up since 0330, dressed in his jungle fatigues, a .45 Colt automatic hung from a web belt around his waist. He has been sitting in his command post, drinking coffee and moving between the staff sections, checking on last-minute progress.

Intelligence (S-2) tells him that the enemy is still there. Surveillance of the assault area by Mohawk airplanes and their infrared sensing devices has seen the enemy as a glow on an indicator, or a symbol on a print-out sheet just as clearly as if they had been standing there in broad daylight waving at the pilot.

Operations and Training (G-3) tells him that, one by one, the vast jigsaw puzzle of supporting units has formed itself. The artillery is ready to begin the barrage. The Air Force is standing by on its runways, waiting for the time to take off.

At 0430, as the troop carriers crank, three helicopters appear over the Ground Tactical Commander's command post, an UH-1D and two HueyCobras. They lose forward speed and settle toward the ground, hover, and finally touch down. The pilot of the UH-1D unstraps himself and slides his door open and walks to the command post.

He is the commander of the Army Aviation elements and the helicopter he has just left is a specially fitted-out machine equipped with a vast assortment of communications equipment. It's the "C-and-C bird," more formally the Command and Control Aircraft. It will serve as a flying command post.

There is a final cup of coffee, as the ground commander and the air commander review a last time the preparations for the assault. Then the ground commander, his S-2 and S-3, and the commander of the aviation elements walk out to the C-and-C ship, strap themselves in and as the rotors increase rpm, the first command passes over the radios:

"All elements, Nancy Jane. Nancy Jane Six airborne."

The HueyCobras take up positions 100-feet above and 50-feet to the rear of the

(U. S. Army Photograph)

(U. S. Army Photograph)

C-and-C aircraft in a "V" formation, as the Huey flies slowly over the pick-up areas, watching as the lines of troops enter the troop carrying helicopters, as the troop carriers go airborne again and begin to form up in the assault formation.

The radios are now busy. The Air Force is on station. The Air Force is commencing its bombing runs. And when they're finished, the artillery begins.

The voice of the artillery spotters, flying their O-1 "Birddogs" comes over the C-and-C earphones. "Right one hundred, down fifty, fire for effect."

The landing zone is now under a heavy artillery barrage, which will continue until, in this case, ten minutes before the troop carriers land. The enemy will not have ten minutes to catch his breath, however, between the time the artillery stops and the landing begins. That period will be taken up by attacks from the HueyCobras, which are already formed up and orbiting near the landing zone.

The troop carriers are now forming up in the air as they move toward their rendezvous point.

The plan has specified the company staggered trail formation for the assault. The company commander, flying a UH-1B gunship, leads the formation. At a 45° to his right rear, his rotor-arc 50-feet away, is the first troop carrier. Fifty feet from him, to his left, is the second troop carrier, directly behind the company commander. Nine more troop carriers follow in a staggered line.

At the tail of the staggered column are two more armed UH-1Bs, each carrying the section commanders. They are at a 45° angle from the column, their rotor arcs 100 feet from the tailing ships.

Behind them are two HueyCobras, 100 feet away.

From different directions, two companies of assault troop carriers, and two platoons

of HueyCobras, an O-1 Birddog and the C-and-C Huey converge on the rendezvous point.

Five HueyCobras, flying in a V formation take up the point, with the Birddog flying above the entire formation.

Immediately behind the HueyCobras is a company of assault troop carriers, with its own gunships and immediately behind them, another five-ship V of HueyCobras.

There are two companies in all, them-

(*U. S. Army Photograph*)

selves formed in a staggered trail and each tailed by a five-ship V of HueyCobras.

Nancy Jane Six, the operation commander, speaks into his microphone as the sweep second hand of the clock on the control panel before him reaches toward twelve:

"This is Nancy Jane Six. Lift the artillery. Commence the assault."

"Big Boy Control," the pilot of the "Birddog" says into his radio. "Cease fire. Stand by."

The mouths of the artillery fall silent, but before the smoke and dust on the landing zone has time to blow away or settle, the first assault by the HueyCobras begins.

They form into a single, follow-me, column and fly a clover-leaf pattern clockwise around the landing zone, timed so that there is never a break in the rocket and grenade and machine-gun fire. As one HueyCobra turns and shuts off his fire, the HueyCobra on his tail begins his weapons attack.

When the last of the first five HueyCo-

(U. S. Army Photograph)

bras has begun the first swing on his attack, the first of a second formation of five HueyCobras takes up its position. For five minutes, the landing zone and the woods at its edges receive a never ending stream of rocket and grenade and machine-gun fire.

And then the first of the troop-carrier formations swings into position, and heads toward the landing zone, losing altitude and speed but never breaking its formation.

The HueyCobras accompanying each company now bring the edges of the landing zone under their guns and the machine guns in the doors of the troop carriers now begin

to fire, spraying the woods and the treelines.

The troop carriers, seemingly all at once, flare, lose forward speed and settle to the ground. Before their skids actually touch, the riflemen start leaping out. As soon as the last man has left the aircraft, the take-off begins. Ten seconds, helpless, on the ground, is considered too long. Half that time is just about par.

Machine guns chattering, the Hueys leap into the air, far more agile now that the weight of their passengers is gone. In formation, with their protective HueyCobras guarding them, they gain speed and altitude and leave the landing zone.

They're not through, however. They move to supply areas where they are re-fueled, rearmed and where they pick up cargo. Some of the cargo helicopters return immediately to the landing zone, as part of a prearranged plan of supply and reinforcement. Some others are loaded with basic loads of ammunition and stand by waiting for a call.

Already from the ground has come the call for a "dust-off." In every war but this one, the red cross on a white background has been respected by the belligerents. But this is Vietnam, and the rules are different. As the first UH-1D marked with the red cross begins to approach the landing zone to pick up its load of wounded Americans, a HueyCobra forms on its tail and circles overhead as the wounded are rushed to the machine.

It returns the enemy fire directed at the ambulance ship and once the ship is air-borne again, makes another assault at the well-concealed, well-dug-in enemy automatic weapons emplacement.

The battalion commander on the ground has been in touch with the commanding officer of Operation Nancy Jane. He is taking automatic weapons fire, and rocket fire, from a dug-in enemy. The only way to get the enemy in his hole is to blast him out.

(*U. S. Army Photograph*)

A mile or two away, the six-man crew of a 105-mm howitzer becomes aware that the rotors of the Chinook in which they have for an hour been sitting are now moving. The sound of the rotors change; there is a slight shudder and the tail of the machine rises a few feet in the air. They're airborne. The Chinook hovers twenty-feet over the ground. A cable is connected to the basic load of ammunition, and above that, to the howitzer (this sling-load is called "a piggyback"). A ground crewman, who has been gesturing with his hands, held at waist level palms up, now makes another motion, a "take it away" gesture.

The Chinook picks up speed and altitude, the howitzer swinging beneath it like a pendulum.

They expect it at the landing zone. Another soldier directs the pilot until the gun is in position. The ammo followed quickly by the howitzer touch the ground and the cable dips slack. It has a "no-pressure-release" mechanism which releases automatically the moment the weight no longer pulls at the connection. The Chinook moves a few feet away to unload the crew. As

soon as the last man is on the ground, the Chinook takes off.

As the gun director gets the target from an infantry sergeant, the gun crew opens the trail, opens the breech, picks up and loads the first round. Sixty-seconds before, they, cannon and crew, had been airborne.

(*U. S. Army Photograph*)

The howitzer fires, and belches smoke and the shell casing comes bouncing out of the breech as another round is loaded. By the time the fifth round is fired at the enemy emplacement, a Chinook, carrying a load in a sling suspended beneath its body hovers near them. It dips to the ground until the load touches releasing the "no-pressure" mechanism. The howitzer has been resupplied with ammunition.

The pilot of the Chinook which had delivered the 105-mm howitzer heads back to his staging area to await further orders. But he doesn't get there right away.

"Stevedore One Niner," his radio says. "This is Stevedore Five. What is your position and status?"

"Stevedore One Nine is Five Minutes from Staging Area Bravo, riding empty."

"Stevedore One Niner, what is your fuel?"

"One Niner has two hours' fuel aboard."

"One Niner, Stevedore Five. You will proceed to Coordinates One Seven Seven Five Two Four. An UH-1D has lost hydraulic pressure and made an emergency landing."

"One Niner understands One Seven Seven Five Two Four," the Chinook pilot repeats the map coordinates as his co-pilot finds the location on the map. All phases of the operation, from the infantry upward, use the Artillery Fire Direction Center's map coordinates.

"Affirmative, One Niner," the radio says. "Downed aircraft is chalk number Victor Seven."

(U. S. Army Photograph)

"One Niner on the way," the Chinook pilot says and banks the huge machine in the direction indicated by the wave of the co-pilot's hand. The co-pilot reaches over his head and tunes in the emergency frequency, 243.0 megacycles.

"Victor Seven," the pilot says, "this is Chinook Stevedore One Niner about three minutes from you. Let's have some smoke."

A new voice comes on the emergency frequency: "Stevedore One Niner, this is Cobra Three Zero with a flight of three. Would you like us to overfly the downed aircraft?"

"Thank you, Cobra Three," the Chinook pilot says. "Where are you?"

"Cobra Three Zero about to overhaul you from three o'clock," the section leader of the flight of three HueyCobras reports over the radio. "I have the smoke in sight."

Moving very fast, forming into a follow-me line as they dip to the ground, the HueyCobras dip toward the narrow column of yellow smoke from the smoke grenade released by the crew of the disabled Huey. Another Huey is circling the area and the tracers from its door guns can be seen lacing the jungle around the small clearing.

"Chinook making approach, this is Victor Eight over the downed Huey."

"Go ahead, Victor Eight," the Chinook pilot says. "I have you in sight."

"The downed aircraft is taking fire from the ridge at the northeast."

"Roger," the Chinook pilot says. "Cobras are now beginning suppressive fire. Will you pick up the crew and the riggers?"

(U. S. Army Photograph)

(*U. S. Army Photograph*)

"Affirmative," the pilot of the Huey says.

The Cobras are now attacking the ridge line as the Chinook hovers over the Huey. A cable unwinds from the Chinook, the Huey crew chief climbs up the side of the Huey, and grabs for the cable. He fastens it to the top of the Huey rotor mast and then jumps off. He stands in front of the machine, signaling with his hands until the Chinook pilot has taken the slack out of the cable. Then he signals for the pilot to "take it away," and the Chinook soars upward, picking the Huey up beneath it.

The other Huey comes in for a quick landing. The crew of the downed Huey and the rigging crew rush toward it and jump aboard. It takes off immediately, following the Chinook.

The shot-down Huey, which had taken machine-gun bullets in its hydraulic system, had been on the ground less than ten minutes. It would fly again. Chinook pilots, aware of the awesome cost of the machine itself and the cost per flight hour of their machine, like to point out that the Chinook has paid its own way in Vietnam by saving other aircraft to fly another day. Without the Chinook downed helicopters and fixed-wing aircraft would either be destroyed by the Viet Cong and North Vietnamese where they fell, or destroyed by the Americans themselves to keep them from falling into enemy hands. The Sikorsky Sky Crane performs the same service for Chinooks in trouble.

The assault and landing phase of the operation is now over. The level of aviation

(U. S. Army Photograph)

activity on the landing zone is now reduced to resupply and evacuation of wounded and prisoners; to gunnery support of the ground troops. Two man Hughes observation helicopters (OH-6As) can be seen now, flitting like small insects over the battle area, serving as eyes for the ground commanders, quite literally airmobile light machine-gun nests.

The fighting goes on all morning, through lunch, and into the early afternoon and then the decision is made to withdraw the ground troops. The enemy has either been destroyed, or has chosen to vanish into the jungle to fight another day.

From staging areas, the troop carriers flutter into the air and return to the landing zone, flying to columns of signal smoke. It takes a little longer, as much as sixty or ninety seconds to load the troop carriers and the HueyCobras fly overhead to protect them during the loading process.

The Chinooks came back and pick up the howitzers and the unfired ammunition and even sling-loads of salvageable brass casings. In forty-five minutes, the landing zone is as deserted of American soldiers as it had been early that morning. All they have left behind is fired small arms cases and here and there empty ration boxes.

The troops are flown back to their base camps and unloaded and finally the helicopters return to their fields. There is a debriefing, a report of damaged aircraft, of wounded personnel, and then a briefing.

There is a new operations order, a search and destroy mission Operation Weary Willie, for the next day. Crank time is 0430.

Index

Italicized page numbers refer to illustrations.